Too Many Clubs And Not Enough Balls

Books by Vernon Coleman

The Medicine Men (1975)
Paper Doctors (1976)
Everything You Want To Know About Ageing (1976)
Stress Control (1978)
The Home Pharmacy (1980)
Aspirin or Ambulance (1980)
Face Values (1981)
Guilt (1982)
The Good Medicine Guide (1982)
Stress And Your Stomach (1983)
Bodypower (1983)
An A to Z Of Women's Problems (1984)
Bodysense (1984)
Taking Care Of Your Skin (1984)
A Guide to Child Health (1984)
Life Without Tranquillisers (1985)
Diabetes (1985)
Arthritis (1985)
Eczema and Dermatitis (1985)
The Story Of Medicine (1985, 1998)
Natural Pain Control (1986)
Mindpower (1986)
Addicts and Addictions (1986)
Dr Vernon Coleman's Guide To Alternative Medicine (1988)
Stress Management Techniques (1988)
Overcoming Stress (1988)
Know Yourself (1988)
The Health Scandal (1988)
The 20 Minute Health Check (1989)
Sex For Everyone (1989)
Mind Over Body (1989)
Eat Green Lose Weight (1990)
Why Animal Experiments Must Stop (1991)
The Drugs Myth (1992)
How To Overcome Toxic Stress (1990)
Why Doctors Do More Harm Than Good (1993)
Stress and Relaxation (1993)
Complete Guide To Sex (1993)
How to Conquer Backache (1993)
How to Conquer Arthritis (1993)
Betrayal of Trust (1994)

Know Your Drugs (1994, 1997)
Food for Thought (1994, revised edition 2000)
The Traditional Home Doctor (1994)
I Hope Your Penis Shrivels Up (1994)
People Watching (1995)
Relief from IBS (1995)
The Parent's Handbook (1995)
Oral Sex: Bad Taste And Hard To Swallow? (1995)
Why Is Pubic Hair Curly? (1995)
Men in Dresses (1996)
Power over Cancer (1996)
Crossdressing (1996)
How to Conquer Arthritis (1996)
High Blood Pressure (1996)
How To Stop Your Doctor Killing You (1996, revised edition 2003)
Fighting For Animals (1996)
Alice and Other Friends (1996)
Spiritpower (1997)
Other People's Problems (1998)
How To Publish Your Own Book (1999)
How To Relax and Overcome Stress (1999)
Animal Rights – Human Wrongs (1999)
Superbody (1999)
The 101 Sexiest, Craziest, Most Outrageous Agony Column
        Questions (and Answers) of All Time (1999)
Strange But True (2000)
Daily Inspirations (2000)
Stomach Problems: Relief At Last (2001)
How To Overcome Guilt (2001)
How To Live Longer (2001)
Sex (2001)
How To Make Money While Watching TV (2001)
We Love Cats (2002)
England Our England (2002)
Rogue Nation (2003)
People Push Bottles Up Peaceniks (2003)
The Cats' Own Annual (2003)
Confronting The Global Bully (2004)
Saving England (2004)
Why Everything Is Going To Get Worse Before It Gets Better (2004)
The Secret Lives of Cats (2004)

novels
The Village Cricket Tour (1990)
The Bilbury Chronicles (1992)
Bilbury Grange (1993)
Mrs Caldicot's Cabbage War (1993)
Bilbury Revels (1994)
Deadline (1994)
The Man Who Inherited a Golf Course (1995)
Bilbury Country (1996)
Second Innings (1999)
Around the Wicket (2000)
It's Never Too Late (2001)
Paris In My Springtime (2002)
Mrs Caldicot's Knickerbocker Glory (2003)
Too Many Clubs And Not Enough Balls (2005)

short stories
Bilbury Pie (1995)

on cricket
Thomas Winsden's Cricketing Almanack (1983)
Diary Of A Cricket Lover (1984)

as Edward Vernon
Practice Makes Perfect (1977)
Practise What You Preach (1978)
Getting Into Practice (1979)
Aphrodisiacs – An Owner's Manual (1983)
The Complete Guide To Life (1984)

as Marc Charbonnier
Tunnel (novel 1980)

with Alice
Alice's Diary (1989)
Alice's Adventures (1992)

with Dr Alan C Turin
No More Headaches (1981)

With Donna Antoinette Coleman
How To Conquer Health Problems Between Ages 50 and 120 (2003)
Health Secrets Doctors Share With Their Families (2005)

Too Many Clubs And Not Enough Balls

Vernon Coleman

Chilton Designs

Published by Chilton Designs, Publishing House, Trinity Place, Barnstaple, Devon EX32 9HG, England

ISBN: 1 898146 80 2

All characters, organisations, businesses and places in this book are fictitious, and any resemblance to real persons (living or dead), organisations, businesses or places is purely coincidental. The golf club which is the setting for this novel exists only in the author's imagination.

A catalogue record for this book is available from the British Library.

Printed by Arrowsmith, Bristol

Dedication

To Donna Antoinette, the Welsh Princess, who'd give you her last ball without hesitation or regret. The sweetest, kindest, most generous-hearted woman a man could ever hope to meet.

Chapter One

'Who The Hell Are You?'

It was cold and I pulled my collar up as I hurried across the car park. The wind was whipping a loose rope against the white painted wood of a tall flag-pole. There was no flag flying. A storm was coming from the West and the dark clouds bloated with the rain they would soon release were hurrying in our direction as though anxious to meet some undeclared deadline. Although it was the middle of the day there were already lights on in the clubhouse.

A long row of wind-battered wooden signs made it clear that the parking spaces nearest to the front door were reserved for the Club Captain, the Club President, the Ladies' Captain, the Ladies' President, the Greens Committee Chairman, the Handicaps Committee Chairman, the Club Secretary and various other dignitaries. An old red Vauxhall and a battered white van were the only vehicles parked there, though neither had been parked well enough to identify the status of the drivers. The owner of the white van had painted out a name on the side of the van with white paint that didn't quite match the original white of the van. Someone had pinned a paper notice to the wooden boards of the clubhouse wall and covered it with clear plastic. The words 'Junior Captain' had been written on the paper in large red capitals but rain had managed to get underneath the plastic and the ink had started to run, making the notice difficult to read and leaving streaky red marks on the paper. The four drawing pins used to hold the notice to the wall had gone rusty and produced brown marks on the plastic.

An old mountain bike, covered in mud, was leaning against the wooden wall, just beneath the paper notice.

Tentatively, I pushed open the right half of a pair of heavy front doors. Both doors were glazed down to waist height and the top halves were virtually covered with small handwritten notices stuck to the glass with peeling sticky tape. The notices were mostly written in capital letters and virtually every sentence ended with at least one (and often two, three or more) exclamation marks. 'Definitely NO spikes in the Lounge!!', 'No dogs EVEN on leads!!!', 'All Visitors must report to the Club Professional's shop!', 'Push hard – door sticks!' and, boasting the greatest number of exclamation marks that I could see, a foolscap sheet of lined paper carrying the following message in a mixture of red and green ink: 'Gentlemen are reminded by the committee that ties and long trousers are compulsory after 6.00 pm and all day on Sundays!!!!'. It wasn't particularly welcoming but I wanted to learn to play golf and the only other local club had a waiting list of six years and, it seemed from a glance at the car park there, a requirement that all members drive something expensive, preferably made in Germany and equipped with personalised number plates. If I was going to play golf this was going to be the place where I was going to learn.

Inside the clubhouse the long corridor which stretched ahead of me seemed about as busy as a school classroom in August. Obeying an instruction pinned to the wall ahead of me I paused for a moment in this golfing equivalent of the Marie Celeste to wipe my shoes on a well-worn doormat which had doubtless once boasted firm bristles, but which now seemed as flat and as abrasive as a sheet of linoleum. It was encrusted with dried mud.

With the soles of my shoes now doubtless muddier than they had been before I tiptoed cautiously along the corridor, feeling very much like a new boy at school.

Both sides of the corridor were lined with notice boards; massive, wooden-framed cork boards which stretched from an inch or two below the ceiling right down almost to knee height. The corridor was, I guessed, about thirty feet long. The boards were at least five feet deep. Of the three hundred square feet of cork available I doubt if a total of more than one remained naked to the world. Every other inch was covered with notices, most of which seemed to contain either a new club rule or an amendment to an old one. I had just begun to work my way through the orders, exhortations and instructions in the hope that I might find one containing information relevant to my own needs, when a door I hadn't noticed (it, too, was covered with corkboard and pinned-on notices) was flung open. The door handle poked through a neat hole which had been cut in the cork board.

'I thought I heard someone come in,' snapped a short, red-faced man. 'About bloody time too.' He wore a blue blazer, a white shirt which hung down almost to his knees and a dark blue tie decorated with a motif showing two crossed golf clubs and a ball. The blazer had gold buttons and a large, impressive-looking badge on the breast pocket. Apart from the dangling parts of his shirt he was naked from the waist down. His feet and lower legs looked wet. He had matching bunions and knees knobbly enough to have won any holiday camp competition.

Confronted with this rather startling sight I instinctively stepped back a pace.

'I've been waiting for you for ages,' he said. 'Follow me.'

Puzzled, but anxious not to make a poor impression, I followed him into a locker room which smelt of a strange mixture of soap, tobacco, perfume and sweat.

'You haven't brought any waders with you?'

'No.'

'Equipment?'

'No.'

'Boots?'

'No. I was hoping to buy what I needed here.' I said. I hadn't heard about the need for waders and none of the golf magazines I'd read had ever mentioned them. I assumed that this might be a local course requirement.

He looked down at my feet. 'You'd better take your shoes and socks off,' he said. 'And your trousers too.'

'I think there's probably some mistake...,' I said.

'Just get 'em off man,' he told me firmly.

Normally, if a man I'd never met before had told me to remove my shoes, socks and trousers I would, I think, have hesitated and wanted answers to some questions. But his request wasn't a request at all, it was an order. And before I could say anything he'd virtually disappeared.

Hurriedly, I tore off my shoes, socks and trousers. What did I know? Maybe golfers had more in common with Freemasons than I'd thought.

'Fourth time it's been blocked this year. I've been trying to clear it myself,' he told me, when I caught up with him. The carpet in the locker room was soaked and water squeezed up between my toes as I walked. 'Heaven knows what they put down the plughole,' he told me over his shoulder. 'I don't want to know. They always say it's long hair but last time it got blocked you chaps fished out an eyebrow brush, a shampoo sachet, a wodge of old tissues and some of those unmentionable things women use.' He paused for a second and looked at me, as though he had noticed something for the first time. 'Don't you even have any rubber gloves?'

'No,' I admitted. 'I thought I'd buy a glove from the professional's shop.' The only thing I knew about golf clubs was that they liked you more if you purchased your equipment from the professional's shop rather than from a golf hypermarket on the industrial estate.

The man in the blazer looked at me as though I might be dangerous and then shrugged. 'I've been using an old putter,' he told me, leading the way down three steps into a flooded shower room. The water had reached the top step of the shower room, which was why the carpet in the locker room was soaked. 'But I've probably just made it worse.' The shower room walls were tiled and as I stepped down into the water it was obvious that the floor was tiled too.

As I waded gingerly through the water, a toilet I hadn't noticed was flushed, a door was opened and a woman of about sixty marched out. She was wearing a tweed skirt, brown woollen stockings and a single string of pearls. I couldn't see what she was wearing on her feet because they were under water. She wore nothing above the waist apart from the pearls. Embarrassed, I looked away and found myself staring at a tall, well-built natural blonde who was standing under one of the showers, back arched, eyes closed, rinsing soap from her hair. Naturally, since she was under the shower, she was wearing nothing either above or below her waist. I looked away, trying desperately to find a direction in which to look which was not laden with the unaccustomed sight of naked female bodies.

'Who the hell are you?' demanded the woman in the tweed skirt.

'He's the plumber,' said the man in the blazer, pointing at me.

'And what the hell are you doing in here Major?' demanded the woman in the tweed skirt, indignant but seemingly unconcerned at finding herself half dressed in front of two men. 'The damned Amenities Committee hasn't made the women's shower unisex has it?'

'The shower drain is blocked,' explained the man in the blazer. 'I do wish you ladies would keep out of the showers while we get the problem sorted out.'

'It's our shower room isn't it? demanded the woman in the tweed skirt. 'What are we supposed to do? Stand outside and wait for it to rain?'

'Expect they'd like us to stand on the patio outside the bar. Throw buckets of soapy water over one another,' said the blonde with a deep-throated guffaw. Other blondes might giggle. She definitely guffawed. She finished rinsing her hair, turned off her shower, pushed her hair back, opened her eyes and, looking in our direction, noticed me for the first time.

'Golly, Mr Secretary,' she said to the man in the blazer. 'Are you doing guided tours of the ladies' shower room now?' She took a large white towel from a hook and, making absolutely no effort to cover her nakedness, started to dry her hair. She did this with such great vigour that it seemed to draw extra attention to her nakedness. I could not help noticing that, in addition to the usual fixtures and fittings, she had extraordinarily well-developed muscles. She reminded me of the female weightlifters one sees alternately grunting and sprinkling themselves with talcum powder at the Olympic games.

'This is the plumber,' replied the club secretary. 'He's come to sort out your blocked drain.'

'Oh, well that makes it OK then,' she drawled. 'Being naked in front of the plumber is like being undressed in front of the doctor.'

'I'm not...,' I said, starting to tell her that I wasn't a plumber.

'Doctors, plumbers and window cleaners,' she said. 'All professionals.' She looked at me and smiled. 'If you weren't a plumber I would scream, call a man and have you arrested,' she said. She guffawed, presumably either at the thought of her screaming or at the thought of her needing to call a man for anything. Mohammed Ali would have retired earlier if he'd had to face the prospect of fifteen rounds with her. 'Major doesn't count,' she added, nodding in the direction of the club secretary.

Suddenly, announcing that I wasn't a plumber didn't sound such a good idea. 'I do bit of plumbing occasionally,' I said, feeling myself reddening. 'More a sort of hobby really. Semi-professional,' I muttered. 'Just drains really. Mainly drains. Not exclusively drains. But mainly drains. Shower drains. Drains in shower rooms.'

'A plumber, eh?' said the woman in the tweed skirt. She looked around her. 'Haven't got a paper and pencil on you I suppose?' she asked the blonde. The blonde confirmed the accuracy of this supposition. The woman in the tweed skirt turned back to me. 'Give me your number before you go, will you? Bloody impossible to find a plumber. I blame the Government. Apart from difficult stuff that requires tools I am devoted to doing it myself. The workmen won't do stuff and want a fortune for it. They never come. I blame New Labour. They've sent everyone to college so that they all have degrees in brewing or media studies and don't want to be plumbers. Did you know that far more people qualify with brewing degrees than as dentists? Could that have anything to do with the fact that half the country is pissed and there aren't enough dentists to go around?'

'I do wish you wouldn't use the shower while the drain is blocked,' said the secretary to the blonde. 'It just makes things worse.'

'You should put up a notice about it,' said the blonde, now drying her back.

'There is a notice about it,' said the club secretary firmly. 'I dictated it myself and you'll find a copy pinned to the noticeboard.'

Not many men could manage to be pompous while not wearing trousers. But the club secretary did it very well. He turned to me. 'Shouldn't you be doing something?' he asked. He pointed to the floor. 'The water's getting deeper.' He was right. The water was getting deeper.

'Er, I'm not quite sure what to do,' I began, rather apologetically. 'Do you have a bucket?'

'I think it's rather late for buckets,' snapped the secretary. 'I'm no expert but I'd have thought that unblocking the drain made more sense.'

'Drain is over here somewhere,' said the blonde, pointing to the far corner of the shower room. I felt around with my feet and I soon found something rather soft and squashy. I bent down, plunged my hand into the water and, during the next few minutes managed to drag out of the water, in quick succession, a pink face flannel, an item of ladies' underwear (blue with lace around the edges), the sort of plastic shower cap given away in hotels, a large, congealed bundle of hair (a mixture of black, brown and blonde), two golf balls, a broken plastic drain cover, a cigar packet, a piece of string about two yards long, a pair of tights and a something which I couldn't identify but which the blonde immediately identified as Mr Roebuck's truss. The secretary's efforts with the old putter had compressed most of these items and, it seemed to me, had almost certainly made the whole situation worse than it might have been.

As I removed the last of these items from the drain the small flood of water disappeared at a most satisfying rate. There was a lot of gurgling.

'Excellent work!' said the club secretary, clapping me on the back. 'Always sensible to call in a professional when you've got a tricky problem.' He peered at the pile of stuff in my hands. 'There's a waste bin in the changing room,' he told me, 'you can toss all that in there.'

'Those are mine,' said the blonde, looking over the items I had removed from the drain and selecting the blue underwear. She picked them out with forefinger and thumb and smiled at me. 'Can't imagine how they got there,' she added.

'I'll have the balls,' said the woman in the tweed skirt, helping herself.

'Don't forget to give Mr Roebuck his truss,' said the blonde.

'Follow me,' said the club secretary, with a sniff. 'After I've shown you the rubbish bin I'll find you a towel.'

'Don't forget to give me your number before you go,' shouted the woman in the tweed skirt.

'I'll have it too,' drawled the blonde. 'Never know when you might need a man with a wrench to give your pipes a bit of a twirl.' She guffawed loudly.

For the first time in several decades I blushed.

Chapter Two

'Everyone Is On A Committee.'

After I had deposited the bits and pieces I had removed from the drain, the club secretary and I dried ourselves on threadbare once-white towels. They had the words PROPERTY OF THE GOLF CLUB – NOT TO BE REMOVED FROM THE BUILDING embroidered on them in faded maroon lettering. I felt much more comfortable when I'd got my trousers, shoes and socks back on.

'Thanks for that,' said the club secretary, when he'd finished double-knotting his shoelaces. 'Must rush. Business to attend to. Tell your people to send along their bill.'

'Actually...' I began, deciding that this might be the appropriate moment to tell him why I was really there. But he'd gone.

I finished tying my shoelaces and then combed my hair in a mirror that was, around the edges, decorated with a mixture of stern warning notices typed on post cards ('Members Are Reminded Not To Leave VALUABLES Unattended In The Locker Room'), promotional cards which had, I assumed, been left by members hoping that fellow members would be inclined to favour work done by a fellow golfer ('Home Perms My Speciality', 'I Guarantee To Help You Lose Up To A Stone A Week', 'Have You Put On Weight Over Christmas? Lady Member Willing To Make Dress Alterations For Fellow Members – Modest Charges' and 'All Your Roofing Needs Attended To Promptly, Work Guaranteed, Member Of The Association Of Roofers' were typical of these) and cards advertising golf products ('Practise Driving In Your Living Room And Add 50 Yards Today'), golfing holidays ('Two

Week Golfing Holidays In Spain – Flights, Accommodation And All Green Fees From £99') and other local courses ('£2 Reduction For Members Of Visiting Clubs On Thursday Afternoons After 6pm From November To March).

As ready as I had been when I had first entered the club half an hour or so earlier (which is to say as ready as I would ever be and not terribly ready at all) I opened the door from the ladies' changing room and stepped out into the corridor directly into the path of a stout, balding man of about 50. He had bright blue twinkly eyes and looked as if he had more fun and worried less than most people. He wore brown and beige checked trousers and a blue jumper which had a tortoise embroidered on the left breast. 'I say, well done you,' he said, with a wink. He looked at his watch. 'Never too early, eh?' He leant a little closer and lowered his voice. 'You might like to do up your fly,' he murmured.

'I was clearing out a drain in the shower room,' I told him, as I pulled up the forgotten zip.

'Never heard it called that before,' he said, looking slightly puzzled. 'Clearing out a drain, eh?' He laughed. He clapped me on the shoulder with a hand like a wicketkeeper's glove. 'Fancy a drink?'

'Actually,' I confessed, 'I really was clearing out a drain and I'm not sure I'm supposed to go into the bar; I'm not entirely a member.'

'Not entirely?'

'Well, to be more precise, not at all. And I did see a notice saying that only members were allowed into the lounge.'

'Oh, don't take any notice of that. Doesn't matter. The whole damned place is festooned with bits of paper telling us what we can't do. If we all read all the notices we'd never do anything else. You can be my guest. My name's Simon.'

'Thank you,' I said. 'I'm Tom. Thank you very much. However, I would like to join the club. Do you think that would be possible?'

He laughed again, louder and for longer.

'You want to what?'

'Join the club.' I repeated. 'If it's possible.'

He laughed again.

'Only if it's possible,' I said. 'If there's a long waiting list...'

'Oh, I would think it's possible,' he assured me with a smile.

'I realise there may be a waiting list,' I said.

He brushed this aside with a wave of one of his massive hands. 'Oh, don't worry about waiting lists,' he said. 'The only place round here with a waiting list is the hospital.'

I followed him along the notice-lined corridor. At the end we turned right. Here, in a shorter corridor, there were more notices on the walls. I glanced at them as we walked by. Whoever had typed them had clearly also been fond of exclamation marks.

'Members Are Advised That This Year's Christmas Dinner Will Be Held On November 26th. The Children's Christmas Party Will Be Held On January 4th. Applications For Tickets Must Be Received By July 17th At Latest!!!!!'

'Members Are Reminded That The Gardens On The Left Of The 8th Fairway Are Out Of Bounds At All Times!!!'

'This Year's July Medal Will Be Held On August 9th!!'

Simon had opened and disappeared through a varnished wooden door. The door carried several plastic notices ('Lounge Bar', 'Members Only',) which had been screwed to the door and which therefore had an air of permanence about them, and numerous paper ones ('Members Must Not Enter Wearing Spikes!!', 'All Drinks Must Be Paid for!!!', 'Gentlemen Must Wear Long Trousers At All Times!!!!' and 'Lady Members Are Requested Not To Climb Onto The Tables While Wearing High Heels!!!!' were the only ones I had time to read) which had been taped into position with sticky tape and which, therefore, had a temporary air to them.

'What's your poison?' asked Simon as I entered the lounge. There was a bar running the full length of the room directly opposite the door. Simon was already sitting on one of a dozen red-topped bar stools.

I hesitated.

'Whisky OK? Malt?'

It seemed a little early in the day for whisky but I didn't like to say so. I mumbled something which even I didn't understand.

'Two malt whiskies,' said Simon to the barman, a tall, lugubrious fellow who wore a waist-length white coat, black trousers, black waistcoat, white shirt and a ready-tied bow-tie which had slipped an inch. 'Laphroaig.' He added before turning back to me. 'It's the only drink which comes out the same colour as it was when it went in,' added Simon. 'Shows it must be good for you.'

'Er, yes, thank you,' I said. I'd never drunk alcohol that early in the day and felt curiously decadent. I reached for my wallet but Simon lifted a hand to stop me. 'My treat,' he insisted. 'You can buy me one when you're a member.'

The barman poured two large whiskies. Simon paid and told the barman to have one himself. 'Always give the barman a drink,' Simon told me. 'Otherwise you'll find that when you totter up to the bar to order a drink he'll suddenly wander off and start vacuuming, fiddling with the till or washing glasses.' I took one of the whiskies and thanked him both for the drink and the advice.

'I'll just pop and see if the club secretary is free,' he told me. He hurried off and disappeared again. I didn't see where he'd gone but he hadn't left through the door through which we'd entered. For a large man he was very good at disappearing.

The barman scuttled off sideways, like a crab, and disappeared from sight. I had no idea where he'd gone either. Now that everyone had disappeared, I looked around.

The lounge was huge, and when it had first been built it had probably looked very elegant. The centrepiece of the wall on the left of the door through which I had entered the room was a huge window which overlooked what I guessed was the eighteenth green. The centrepiece of the opposite wall was a massive stone fireplace. The hearth was piled high with grey ash, blackened remnants of wood and discarded crisp and cigarette packets. There were half a dozen huge leather arm chairs in front of the fireplace and half a dozen mis-matched chairs and sofas positioned so that the occupants could look out of the window. The leather chairs were badly scuffed and worn and several had tears in their leather with the stuffing poking out. Everything had probably once been rather glorious. Now it was all rather faded. The small tables, liberally sprinkled with beermats and ugly ashtrays advertising a variety of alcoholic beverages, were marked with hundreds of tiny holes. Little hillocks of wood dust on the carpet suggested that the woodworm responsible were still in residence.

The carpet had probably been expensive when first bought but it had long since lost its pile and at a dozen or more places around the room had worn right through so that the rapidly thinning underfelt was itself visible. The walls were decorated with huge old oil paintings in gilt frames. In between the pictures the walls were decorated with damp patches. The oil paintings were so dirty that they made little more sense than the damp patches.

'I've found the club secretary,' said Simon, striding purposefully back into the lounge through a door I hadn't even noticed. The man in the blazer followed closely behind him holding a piece of paper and beaming.

'It's the plumber!' said the club secretary when he saw me.

'Gosh!' said Simon. 'Are you a plumber? What wonderful luck. You fellows are rarer than astronauts. Could you pop round to the house sometime and take a look at one of our bathroom taps. Damned thing has been dripping for months.'

'I'm not actually a plumber,' I said. I took a gulp of my whisky. This, I felt, was probably going to be confusing for everyone, including me.

'Of course he's a plumber,' said the club secretary to Simon. 'He's just cleared the drain in the ladies' changing room.' 'I'm not really a plumber,' I insisted. 'But I had to say that because of the woman in the shower.'

'Aha! Oh yes. I understand!' said Simon. 'Brilliant. Plumber eh?' He winked again. 'Gets you into showers and bathrooms and all sorts of private places. Must try that sometime.'

'He's a plumber,' insisted the club secretary, raising his voice. 'He cleaned out the drain in a jiffy.'

Simon moved a little closer and lowered his voice. 'There's nothing wrong with being a plumber,' he assured me. 'We've got one member who's a traffic warden and another who's an estate agent. We're not snobby round here. For heaven's sake we've even got dentists and lawyers as members.'

'Thank you,' I said.

Simon turned to the club secretary. 'Our new friend the plumber wants to join the club. Have you got the forms?'

'Why do you want to play golf?' the secretary asked me.

I thought about this for a moment. I was concerned that my answer might affect my application. I didn't want to admit that I was playing because my doctor had told me I needed the exercise and my mother had said that I either played golf or got married. 'Bit of fun,' I guess. 'Gentle exercise. Fresh air. Good companions. Tottering around the course, idly flicking a ball here and there. Looking at the birds and the butterflies. Getting out in the sunshine. Getting away from the rat race. Leaving my responsibilities behind for a while. Having a few hours away from the stress and competition of daily life.'

This was greeted with silence. Simon and the secretary looked at me as if I had suddenly turned purple and sprouted huge feathery wings.

'Have I said something wrong?' I asked.

'No, no, not at all,' said Simon. 'But you have to understand that some of the people here are members of the club for, er, other reasons. They like the politics and the pressure. They enjoy the responsibility and the authority.'

'Oh,' I said, genuinely surprised.

'But whatever your reasons for wanting to join I'm sure you'll be glad you did,' said the secretary.

'Right,' I said. 'Do you enjoy golf?'

'Enjoy golf?'

'The game. Hitting little white balls around.'

The secretary looked at me as though I was barking mad. 'Never played the game,' he said. He laughed. 'Damned silly game as far as I can see.' He shrugged as though dismissing the strange tastes of people who chose to play golf as of little consequence. He walked over to the bar, wiped away a puddle, and put the piece of paper he was carrying down on the dry part of the bar. 'If you'd just sign here,' he said.

'Can I join straight away?' I asked surprised. Despite Simon's reassurance I had still expected there to be a waiting list of some sort. I'd heard of prospective golfers having to wait years to join a club and spending their weekends hanging around outside the club entrance hoping to see an ambulance drive in through the gates to take away an existing member mortally afflicted with a stroke or heart attack.

'I think we can squeeze you in,' said the club secretary drily.

'How many new members have joined up this year?' Simon asked him.

'It's been a trifle on the quiet side recently.'

'None?' asked Simon.

'Approximately none,' agreed the club secretary. 'We should do more advertising perhaps. Get ourselves known.'

'Might attract the wrong sort of person,' said Simon.

'Precisely my thought,' agreed the club secretary, handing me his pen.

I signed my name. 'It says here that I need to be proposed and seconded by two members who've known me for at least two years and can vouch for my good standing,' I pointed out.

'I'll propose you,' said Simon, whom I had known for probably the best part of a quarter of an hour. 'You're standing and that's good enough for me.' He scribbled his signature on the form. 'Now you need a seconder,' he said. He looked around. Apart from the three of us and the barman the lounge was completely empty.

'Albert would have been happy to do that,' said the club secretary, taking the form. 'I'll sign for him to save him the trouble.'

'Who's Albert?' I asked.

'Nice old chap,' said Simon. 'You'd have liked him. Used to spend every day in that chair over there.' Simon nodded towards the fireplace. 'He died in it last Wednesday. He was 92.'

'I'll put last Tuesday's date on the form,' said the secretary. 'Just in case anyone ever looks. Though I can't imagine why they would.'

'Great!' said Simon. 'Now you're a member and you can buy us both a drink.' He called the barman over and ordered three whiskies. I took out my wallet and paid the barman. 'Have a drink yourself,' I told him, remembering Simon's advice.

'Just one more thing to be done,' said the club secretary. He turned to me with a big smile. 'A cheque please.' He pointed to the form. 'That's the joining fee and that's the first year's membership fee.'

I took out my cheque book.

'Would you like a locker?' asked the secretary.

I must have looked as puzzled as I felt.

'You definitely want a locker,' said Simon. 'Great for keeping your stuff in. Things you don't want the accountant or your wife to find.'

Not having an accountant or a wife I felt that my need for a locker might not be great. But I didn't like to admit this. 'OK. Yes please. I'd like a locker.'

'That'll be another £15.73,' said the secretary. 'As a deposit. I'll then put your name on the waiting list. Once you get a locker there's a £25 a year rental fee payable.'

'There's a waiting list for lockers?'

'I'm afraid so. We've got 351 members, of whom 278 are men. But there are only 117 male lockers.'

'Ah. How long is the waiting list?'

'Well really you've just got to wait until someone resigns or dies,' explained the secretary. 'People don't resign very often but we do have vacancies for the, er, other reason.'

'So, how long do you think I'll have to wait?'

'Well there are 161 people on the waiting list,' said the secretary. 'So it's just a matter of fate, really. A cold snap during the winter could liberate half a dozen lockers.'

'Mind you, when there were five sudden deaths among locker holders a few years ago there was some talk of calling in the police,' said Simon.

'That was nothing more than hysteria,' snorted the secretary. 'The police were never called.'

'But all the dead members did have lockers.'

'Most of the locker holders are senior members,' the secretary pointed out.

Two minutes later, in return for my membership cheque, I was handed a small plastic disk with a piece of string attached to it. In return for my cheque for a locker deposit I was offered a small slip of paper on which the word 'Reciept' was printed and misspelt.

'That's your membership disk,' said the club secretary, handing me the plastic disk as though he was awarding me an Olympic gold medal. 'Tie it to your golf bag immediately and keep it there at all times.'

'I don't have a golf bag,' I told him.

'What do you keep your clubs in?'

'I don't have any.'

'Oh, I think you'll need some clubs,' said the club secretary. He looked at Simon. 'Won't he?'

'Definitely need some clubs,' said Simon.

'Let Simon take you along to the professional's shop,' said the secretary. 'He's on the amenities committee. He can probably get you a discount.'

'You're on a committee?' I asked Simon. I was impressed.

'Everyone is on a committee,' he told me. 'We've got dozens of them. Competitions Committee. Greens Committee. Finance Committee. Handicap Committee. Ladies' Committee. Veterans' Committee. Billiards Committee. Management Committee. Maintenance Committee. Fixtures Committee. We've got more committees and sub-committees than the House of Commons. We've got 350 members and 340 of them are on at least one committee.' He grinned. 'We'll get you on a committee before long,' he promised. 'But I'm afraid no one can get you much of a discount.'

Chapter Three
'Buy Some Bats And Mauve Trousers.'

When I conducted an impromptu and utterly unscientific survey of fellow club members to find out why they had started playing the game I was not exactly startled to find that no one had begun for the same reason that I had.

Four out of fifteen golfers questioned admitted (one of them with some reluctance) that they had started playing golf because they thought it would be good for business and that by the time they had found that it wasn't, it was far too late to stop. They were too far in to go back.

Three out of the fourteen told me, rather shamefacedly, that they had joined the golf club in order to improve their social lives and enhance their social standing. One of the three confessed that he had joined the club in the hope that it might help him meet a nubile young woman. When I asked them if their ambitions had been realised one was too drunk to understand the question, one said he wasn't going to answer because his friends might read his reply and cut him and the third (the one who had joined hoping to find a wife) confessed that he didn't think he'd be able to remain a member much longer because the alimony payments were killing him.

Three told me that they had been attracted to the game after discovering how much money the top professionals can make. After an average of four years playing the game one of this trio had got his handicap down to 16, one had a handicap of 22 and the third had never got round to getting an official handicap at all. Their gross cumulative winnings since taking up golf amounted to £23.85, of which £3.85 had been taken out of the club's fruit machine and the rest had been won in the club's annual sweepstake on the Grand National.

One fellow told me that he had started playing golf because he had inherited a set of golf clubs, a pair of shoes and a trolley. When he'd taken the whole lot to a second-hand shop he'd been offered such a derisory sum that he'd decided to join the local club and use them himself. He said he'd once worked out that if he included membership fees, balls, equipment, rounds of drinks and so on, his inheritance had cost him £34,548. He said if you factored in the money he would have earned if he'd done something more useful with his evenings and weekends the total sum he'd lost would have been closer to £100,000.

One said he'd joined the club after moving into a house nearby. He said it had seemed a pity not to take advantage of the club's proximity.

One told me that he had joined because his marriage was in trouble and he thought that having a hobby might help make him a more interesting person. He said that he discovered that while he was out on the golf course his wife was having an affair with their marriage guidance counsellor. He kept up his membership after the divorce, even though paying the fees took up most of the money he was left with, because he had no where else to spend the evenings.

One member told me he couldn't remember why he had joined but that he'd done lots of stupid things he couldn't explain and the final member I questioned told me that he had only joined because both his father and his mother were members. He said he thought they had discovered that the annual cost of a junior membership was considerably less than the cost of hiring babysitters two or three times a week.

* * *

I can remember exactly why I decided to start playing golf. It was no idle whim, no passing fancy translated into action simply through a lack of urgency to do anything else.

I did not start playing golf because I wanted to improve my

social life, acquire more customers or enhance my social standing. And I did not start playing golf because of any family connection. (Though it is perfectly true that I did have an uncle who used to make a tidy sum in beer money by picking golf balls out of a stream behind the 10th green at his nearest club. He was so well known to the members that they would approach him as he waded up and down the stream in his Wellington boots, feeling for balls with his feet and picking them out of the mud with his bare hands.)

I started to play golf because my doctor told me to.

Well, he didn't actually tell me to start playing golf.

But, after a routine insurance examination during which he had sucked in air faster than a vacuum cleaner, he did tell me that I needed to take up some exercise, find a hobby and get out more.

'You're overweight and out of shape,' he told me. 'If you were a horse I wouldn't let you race. Your blood pressure is too high and you're as stressed as a politician on election night.'

When I told him that he could either treat me or horses but not both, he responded by showing me the form he'd more or less finished filling in for my insurance company.

'You're in excellent condition for a man waiting for a congratulatory telegram from the Queen,' he told me. 'If you were 99 I'd clap you on the back, buy you a whisky and tell you to cut down on the cigars and carry on as before.'

'Well there you are then,' I answered, full of false joie de vivre.

'I don't know why these people are offering to take your money,' he told me, pointing to the insurance form. 'If I had shares in their outfit I'd sell them and buy something less risky – like a swimsuit store in Antarctica.' He scribbled something else on the form, signed it, folded it and stuffed it into a large brown envelope. 'I've told them that I've advised you to take up a regular exercise programme. It'll be one of the policy conditions.'

'I have to start exercising?'

He nodded.

'So, which sport do you reckon I should take up?' I asked him. 'Darts? Snooker? Plenty of exercise there, surely.' I tossed an imaginary dart at the wall over his head.

'You need to get yourself out in the fresh air,' he told me.

'I think I've torn something,' I complained, rubbing my shoulder. 'I threw that dart too hard.'

'Regular long walks,' he said, ignoring my moan. 'Get away from telephones and computers for a few hours a week. Find a sporting hobby that will capture your imagination and your heart.'

'I lolled around on a barge on the Loire for a couple of weeks three years ago,' I pointed out. 'I could try that again.'

'No, no,' he said. 'You don't need a holiday. You need to change your life. You need regular exercise. Out of doors. You need to expose yourself to the elements; move around, get face to face with nature occasionally.'

'How about rally driving?' I suggested, ignoring the bit about exposing myself to the elements. 'I rather fancy driving one of those souped up four-wheel drive saloons on icy roads.'

'Golf,' he said firmly. 'You'll get plenty of gentle exercise and all the fresh air you can breathe. Ball. Stick. Hit one with the other and get it into the hole. How difficult can that be? I expect they have rules but it can't be that hard. And there's a bonus – it'll give you a chance to meet people with a similar outlook on life.'

I looked at him and raised an eyebrow.

'Forget that,' he said, raising a hand in apology and correcting himself. 'You're not going to find anyone with a similar outlook on life. But you'll meet some real eccentrics. I often used to wonder if people did it to wear the clothes or wore the clothes to do it. Then I discovered that a friend of mine plays golf. Perfectly normal in every other respect, though he is a gynaecologist. He swears he plays golf because he loves the clothes. He normally dresses very conservatively. Pinstripe suit. He does wear a bow tie. But, of course, a lot of gynaecologists wear bow ties...'

'Why?' I interrupted.

'Oh, it's because if they wear ties they always get in the way. My fiancée gave me a tie for Christmas one year when I was a medical student doing obstetrics. On Boxing Day I stitched it into a woman's perineum which I was repairing after she'd given birth to a ten pound baby. She didn't speak to me again.'

'The patient?'

'My fiancée. I had to throw the tie away. It was silk. She thought

I'd lost it. Gave me my ring back and married a psychiatrist.'

'I'm sorry.'

'Oh don't be. She was quite a harridan and a pain in the neck too. She was the only person I ever met who worried about becoming a hypochondriac. Most people worry that they've got cancer or dicky hearts. She worried that she might become a hypochondriac. She married a psychiatrist. Perfect match.' He was silent for a moment and shuddered, as though the memory of the woman he'd nearly married had upset him. 'My pal the gynaecologist says the golf course is the only place where he can dress up like a pimp and fit in perfectly,' he continued. 'I gather they call him Dickory down at the club where he plays.'

'Odd name.'

'He plays with old-fashioned hickory shafted clubs.'

'I don't, er, quite understand.'

'Hickory, dickory doc.'

'Ah.'

'He's a doctor, you see.'

'Yes. I get it now.'

'So, get yourself some lime green trousers, a lilac shirt and a pair of two-tone correspondent shoes and you'll fit right in.' He looked at me. 'Do golfers wear hats?'

'I don't know.'

'Have to be a huge purple fedora if they do,' he said.

I was half way to the door when he suddenly remembered something. 'Oh, I nearly forgot,' he said, scribbling something on his prescription pad. 'Take these.'

'What are they?' I asked him.

'Oh just stuff to make you feel better,' he said.

'Can I drink with them?'

'You can drink whisky, milk, cocoa or parsnip wine with them for all I care,' he said, with a dismissive wave of the hand. 'They're only a placebo to make us both feel I've done something useful.'

When I got home that evening my mother rang. She loves to interfere in my life and, knowing that I had an insurance medical booked, had wasted no time in ringing my doctor to get my results and then ringing me to let me know that she knew them. When doctors become doctors they swear not to divulge confidences about their patients. But none of that means anything when they talk to my mother. The Government should hire her as an interrogator. They wouldn't need to torture suspects. My mother could get anyone to talk in an hour. She just wears them down.

'So, you're going to start taking regular exercise?' she said. It was a question, but only just.

'I thought what went on in a consulting room was supposed to be confidential,' I complained, mildly.

'Don't be silly,' said my mother. 'I'm your mother.'

'Right,' I agreed.

'So you're going to start playing golf.' It was no longer a question.

'Definitely,' I said. I am a bachelor, rather comfortably set in my ways and not a reckless man, I do not argue with my mother. You may call this cowardice. I prefer to think of it as self-preservation.

'Splendid,' she said. 'About time too. It's either that or find yourself a nice girl and get married.'

'Marry?'

'You don't eat properly,' said my mother. 'A nice girl will cook for you and make sure you eat proper meals. Good food. Nicely prepared and properly cooked. Hot meals three times a day.' I looked at the bag of chips I'd picked up on the way back from the doctor's. 'I've got a hot meal ready,' I told her. 'It's going cold as we speak but I've got a hot meal on the table.'

'Chips,' said my mother, for whom the invention of the video phone was a complete waste of time. 'A bag of chips. That's not balanced food.'

'You mean I've either got to take up exercise or get married?'

'It's one or the other' said my mother firmly. 'For your health. I'm saving your life here. No arguments.'

'Exercise or marriage?'

'Golf,' said my mother. 'Not just exercise. Golf's the best for you. Fresh air. Nice people.'

'But I might not be any good at it,' I protested. I wasn't too keen on the idea of taking up golf. The other alternative wasn't even in the frame. I could just about put up with spending my

Sunday mornings trudging through mud in search of small white balls, but marriage seemed a prospect too awful to contemplate.

'Of course you will,' said my mother. 'You'll be wonderful. You'll have lessons. Buy some bats and mauve trousers and you'll be winning mugs and things in no time. You'll be on the television.'

'Right,' I said.

'Golf,' she said. 'And, who knows, maybe you might meet a nice young girl as well.'

'Right,' I said. 'Golf it is.'

And so golf it was.

Chapter Four

'What Do You Want?'

The golf club shop was more of a shed than a shop and looked very much like the sort of cabin builders erect on building sites so that they've got somewhere dry to boil a kettle on days when it's too wet to work, somewhere shady to read the sports pages on days when it's too hot to work and somewhere private to meet when discussing industrial action.

I discovered later that the shed had been added on to the main clubhouse as a temporary measure back in the 1970s. It had been intended that it would last no more than six months, but the club had never got round to replacing it. This may have had something to do with the fact that the architect who had been hired to draw up plans had an unusual and expensive penchant for adding minarets to everything he built. A bizarre and much photographed flat-roofed public lavatory with minarets at both ends was the only known physical manifestation of his visions.

The cabin had white panel walls and a flat roof which had been destined to leak when it had been erected and which, the water stains showed, had fulfilled that destiny many times. The walls had cracked in several places and although the original colour scheme had relied heavily on the colour white, nature had added several patches of green which, on closer inspection, appeared to be the result of a type of fungus. The whole sorry-looking structure was resting on six piles of crumbling cheap bricks and approached by three rather rickety wooden steps. The windows were grimy but I could just make out the figure of a tall golfer in a patterned jumper standing looking out of a grimy window. The golfer, whom, to my surprise I vaguely recognised, looked alert, erect and dignified and appeared to be staring hard at something in the distance; this made him look distracted, as though his mind had managed to escape the end which had befallen his body.

'I'll leave you here,' said Simon. 'Got to be getting back to the bar. Pop in afterwards and let me know how you get on?

'You're not coming in?' I had rather hoped that Simon might help me choose my new clubs.

'Not if you don't mind,' he said rather apologetically. He leant towards me and lowered his voice. 'To be honest I don't particularly want to see the professional. I started a course of refresher lessons some time ago and never quite got round to finishing them.'

With a small wave and an apologetic look, Simon hurried back towards the bar.

When I stepped inside the shop the floor sagged under my weight and as I took a stride forward the whole building shook as though about to fall down. Inside the shop the walls were lined with racks of shiny, brand new golf clubs. There was a desk at one end of the shop and at the other a dozen empty golf bags leant against one another for support. The price labels attached to the bags, which swayed gently as I walked, suggested that they were new. The patches of mildew on the bags suggested that they had been there for some time. As the building continued to sway one of the bags moved away from the others and fell noisily to the floor. The golfer in the patterned jumper turned out to be a full size cut-out advertising a brand of golf club. My diagnosis had been half correct. There was no mind but there was no body either.

I turned gingerly towards the desk, behind which there was an empty red chair, the sort typists use. Since there was no one sitting in it I could see that the seat of the chair was worn and had, in several places, been repaired with black insulating tape. The desk was piled high with packets containing golf balls, golf tees, golf gloves, scorecards, pencils and sweets. If I had found this shabby little shop anywhere else in the world I would, despite all the colour, have found it depressing and rather sad. But here, as the window to a new world, I found it rather exciting.

'Who are you and what the hell do you want?' demanded a voice.

I turned round. 'I've just joined the club,' I told the owner of the voice; a short, thickset man wearing pink trousers and a matching pink sweater. I had no idea where he had been hiding. Both the trousers and the sweater he was wearing were decorated with green triangles outlined in cream. The word 'Plug' and a yellow elephant were embroidered on the front of the sweater. The whole effect was vaguely nauseating. The swaying of the shop made things worse.

'Ah,' he said, making no effort to hide the satisfaction he clearly felt at meeting a new customer. He would have probably rubbed his hands together if he hadn't been holding a large cardboard box.

'I'm Walter,' he said. 'Golf professional here. Been the professional for 34 years. I know every member by name. Used to be on the professional circuit when I was younger but gave it up. Not my cup of tea. I like working with people.'

I told him my name. When I added that I had never played golf before his smile broadened.

'You'll need clubs then,' he went on, tossing the cardboard box to one side and turning to me with ill-suppressed eagerness. 'Do you know anything about the game?'

'Nothing much,' I admitted. 'Ball. Club. Long walk on the grass. Give the ball a clump with the club every now and again. Lots of fresh air. Huge amount of money if you win anything.' I smiled. He tried to smile back. He was just too polite to rub his now unencumbered hands together with glee but he couldn't stop his eyes lighting up with excitement.

'Some beginners start off with a half set, but believe me that's a huge mistake,' said the professional. 'It's like trying to save money by going into a shop for a pair of shoes and buying just one shoe instead of two. It'll just start you off on a bad footing.' He paused, examined me carefully as though trying to decide whether or not to buy shares in me, looked around and lowered his voice a little. 'Unless it's a matter of money, of course. Some people can't afford a whole set. For them a half set is an essential compromise.'

'Oh no, it's not a question of money. Of course not,' I replied, laughing lightly and snapping out the response like a trout taking a fly. 'Oh no, I don't want to go off half-cocked. Full set. The works. One of each. Maybe some spares if you think it best. No half measures.'

'We'll start with a set of irons,' said the professional, turning round and pulling some golf clubs out of a rack.

'Golly,' I said. 'All of these? Are they breakable?'

'Breakable? No.'

'I just wondered if that was perhaps why I needed so many.'

'You've got a 2,3,4,5,6,7,8 and 9, a sand iron and a couple of wedges.' He pulled a club from a rack. 'Try this,' he suggested, handing me the club he'd selected.

I took the club from him. The top part of the shaft was covered with a smart-looking red and black grip. The bottom part of the shaft was shiny. Right at the end of the shaft, the business end as my father would doubtless have put it, the manufacturer had glued a chunky piece of metal. This also shone, though not as brightly as the shaft.

'Hold it with both hands,' he said.

I wrapped both hands round the leather handle at the top of the shaft.

'You haven't played at all before, then?'

'No.' I looked down and then up at him. 'Is it that obvious?'

'Not even a round on a seaside pitch and putt course?'

'No.' I hesitated, remembering. 'Actually, I played two holes of a crazy golf course in Devon. It was some time ago.'

'Just two holes?'

'I lost the ball they gave me. They said I'd have to give them a £10 deposit if I wanted another. So my Mum took me for some chips and we left my Dad to finish off by himself. He went round in 143 which was, so he told us, the 12th best score of the afternoon. He finished all nine holes too. Including the long, difficult one that has the hole at the top of a little concrete castle surrounded by a moat.'

'Just out of interest, how on earth did you manage to lose a ball on a crazy golf course?'

'It bounced off one of the sails of the windmill, hit a huge concrete monkey and disappeared over the wall. I wanted to go after it but my Mum wouldn't let me. She said there was too much traffic.'

Walter made a strange humming noise.

'I don't think anyone was hurt,' I said. 'Not badly.'

'That must have been a relief.'

'But when I went back the following year they had erected a twelve foot high netting fence around the course. I was keen to have another go but the chap who was selling the tickets recognised me and said he'd call the police if I didn't leave him alone.'

'What a pity.'

'But that was all a long time ago,' I said, with a light laugh. 'And I doubt if you have many windmills or concrete monkeys on your course.'

'No,' agreed the professional. He cleared his throat and made it clear from his body language that he was about to tell me an Important And Significant Story. 'I once went for nine months without losing ball,' he began. 'Played every day – twice some days – and never lost a single ball. That was just after I nearly won the Open.'

'You nearly won the Open?' I said, impressed. Even I had heard of the Open Championship.

'Led for the first two rounds,' said Walter, as though embarrassed to share this with me. 'Then things didn't go my way. Bad luck. Always been my problem. Bad luck. I came sixth in the end. My best ever finish. Still, wasn't to be.'

I told him how sorry I was to hear this.

'Try and put your hands a little closer together.'

I moved my hands closer.

'Touching.'

I complied.

'Not so tightly and not as if you were holding an axe.'

I relaxed my fingers a little and saw the blood begin to flow back into my knuckles.

'Golf is a very delicate game,' said the professional. 'It's all about feel. The club must become an extension of your body.'

I looked down and tried to think of the club as part of my body. I wiggled it about.

'Don't worry about it,' said the professional, picking up the lifesize cardboard cut-out that I had knocked over. 'There isn't much room in here.'

I took an imaginary swing. Too late the professional tried to stop me. There was a lot of noise, as though glass had broken. I felt something land on my head.

Gingerly I lowered the club.

'If you stand very still I'll pick the pieces of glass out of your hair,' said the professional.

'I'm sorry about that.'

'It doesn't matter,' insisted the professional, in that way people have when you know they mean that it really does and although they don't want to offend you by telling you outright how much it matters, they nevertheless want you to know that by telling you that it doesn't matter they are doing you a favour and you are, therefore, indebted to them and going to have to end up paying for what you've done far more heavily than if they had been honest, told you how much it mattered and given you a bill. 'The lamp shade was old and the bulb hadn't been changed for months so it was probably near the end of its life anyway.'

'I'm very sorry,' I apologised, again.

'Don't worry about it. The official price for these is £745,' said the professional. 'But since you're a new member I can give you a discount.'

'Thank you,' I said.

'We have a special introductory discount scheme for new members.' He reached past me and picked up a calculator from his desk. 'You get a 1% discount on all new clubs so that would give you...' He fiddled with the calculator. 'A discount of £7.45.' He thought for a moment, trying to deduct £7.45 from £745. 'Oh what the hell,' he said. 'Let's make it a round figure. You can have them for £740.'

'Thank you.'

'And I'll throw in a small packet of tees.'

'That's very kind of you,' I said. 'Actually I prefer coffee if that's possible.'

The professional looked at me, puzzled.

'Instead of the packet of teas,' I said. 'Coffee.'

'Tees,' said the professional. He spelt it out for me. 'To support your balls.'

'Oh. Right. Of course.' I didn't have the foggiest idea why, where or when my balls would need supporting but I'd clearly made a faux pas of some kind so I shut up.

'It's a matched set,' he said, taking the club from me and lovingly running his fingers up and down the shaft. 'Genuine steel shafts. Made in Japan by skilled, dedicated craftsmen.'

'Right,' I said. 'I have a television set made by the Japanese. It's very good. And I know someone who had a Japanese car. Not a great deal of room inside but nicely finished. They make motorbikes too, I understand. And pianos. Versatile people.' I knew I was rambling but couldn't stop myself. The professional made me uncomfortable. 'Considering their limited size,' I added.

'These are very well made. It's a reputable company. The company is not well known but that's because they prefer to spend money on improving the product rather than on advertising, marketing and sponsoring professionals on the Tour.'

'Good. Very good. I'm glad you suggested Japanese. I think it's important that we forget about the war. It was all a long time ago. My great uncle once helped them build a very good railway I believe. Before he died he was in a very forgiving mood. He forgave his wife for her indiscretions and he said he forgave the Japanese for what they'd done to him. We all thought it was very noble of him. Though we did wonder if he wasn't perhaps trying to get a few brownie points in the bag before he met the, er, Big Guy upstairs.'

'You won't buy better than these at the price,' the professional told me. 'Not unless you go to one of those discount stores of course. Or go mail order. But then you don't get the level of service, do you?'

'Hello Walter,' said a cheery voice. We both looked round. A man of about sixty strode firmly towards us. He had a white handlebar moustache, a sunburnt scalp and huge amounts of hair growing out of his ears. He wore plaid trousers, of which the predominant colour was green, and a mauve mohair sweater with dark purple piping around the neck and wrists.

'Can I have half a dozen of your cheap, second-hand balls Walter?'

'Who the hell are you?'

'Hargreaves,' said the newcomer.

'Where did you get that jumper?'

'Not sure old man. My wife bought it for me for my birthday. One of the shops in town, I expect. Like it, do you? I could ask her if you like. She'll know. Always knows where she buys things.'

'You didn't get it here, did you?'

'No, I don't think so, Walter. Afraid not. I have bought stuff from you though. Socks I remember particularly.'

'Bugger off. I'm not selling you cheap balls if you can't be bothered to buy your expensive sweaters here.'

The prospective customer stalked off, rather redder in the face than he had been when he'd arrived.

'You haven't given me any of those clubs with the big bulbous ends,' I pointed out when the prospective customer had gone and Walter and I were alone once more. 'Shouldn't I have one or two of those? Aren't they used for whacking the ball off the flat green bit? I've seen them on the television.'

Walter, clearly still raging inside at his would-be customer's faithlessness took a moment to recover his composure. 'Woods? Oh yes. Absolutely. But they come separately, of course. I suggest a driver, three wood and five wood.' He took three clubs from another rack and handed them to me. I held the three clubs, terrified of dropping them or breaking something with them.

'These are quite a bargain,' said the professional. 'You couldn't find better. Perfect for a beginner but they'll grow with you. Last you years.'

'What about a two wood and a four wood? Shouldn't I have those as well?'

'You're only allowed 14 clubs,' the professional reminded me.

I counted up the irons and the three woods. 'Thirteen.'

'You'll need a putter.'

'Of course.'

'You'll obviously want a sprung socket putter, with a coated face.'

'Obviously. Oh yes.'

'I've got one here,' said the professional, taking yet another club from the rack. 'It's the spitting image of the big money putter. But this one will cost you £15 less than the brand leader you've probably seen advertised in the magazines. If you can tell the difference you let me know.'

'Right.'

'Just £189.99 instead of....' Walter scratched his head. 'More than that. Around £15 more anyway. I did work out the prices once.' He looked around, searching for a catalogue or magazine.

'Splendid.' I said.

The professional abandoned his search almost as quickly as he had started it. 'The brand leader has that little bit cut out at the back,' he said. 'That's really the only difference. And the titanium shaft. Otherwise they're pretty much identical. Except that you're paying £15 less.'

'Good.

'£15 doesn't sound much but when you're buying 14 brand new clubs every pound saved is another pound to spend on balls. That's what I always tell my customers.'

'Are you sure I really need 14 clubs?' I asked, suddenly overcome by an attack of thrift. 'I thought it was balls golfers lost – not clubs.'

'All the professionals carry 14,' said the professional. 'It's the approved number.'

'Why 14?' I asked him. 'Just out of interest. Why not 18?'

He looked at me. It was clearly not a question he had ever heard asked before. It was certainly not a question he had asked himself.

'I'm not sure,' he replied. He thought for a moment. 'I suspect it's the most clubs the average man can carry round a golf course.'

I nodded. 'That would explain it,' I agreed. 'If you had, say, 41 clubs you'd need a whole team of caddies to carry them round for you. If you had 141 clubs you'd need a big truck. And the course would soon get pretty crowded.'

He looked at me blankly and nodded back.

'Besides,' I added. 'It would take for ever to decide which club to use. Say, for example, that every golfer had 100 clubs. Or 1,000. It would take a chap absolutely ages to decide which club to use. Instead of just pulling out his number 6 or whatever he'd be stuck for choice. Trying to decide whether to use a number 450 or a number 451.'

'Yes,' said the professional. 'I suppose so.' He took a pace backwards.

'Do I take them all with me at once?'

'Of course.'

'I'll need some sort of container,' I said, looking round. 'Something to tie them all together.' I picked up a handful of clubs. Several slipped out of my clutch and fell to the floor. 'An old cardboard box perhaps? A black bin liner would do.'

'We have special bags,' said the professional. I felt stupid. I wanted to tell him, but didn't, that I had known that. He walked down his shaky shop, selected a huge blue and white plastic golf bag and brought it back to show me. 'I recommend this bag,' said the professional. 'Made of genuine plastic covered with a patented waterproofing resin compound. All the fitments are genuine brass colour and the zips are heavy duty double action and fully guaranteed for the life of the bag.' He played with a zip which seemed stuck. 'They're firm,' he told me. 'You don't want loose zips or else all your stuff will fall out as you go round the course. This bag will carry all your clubs and protect them from scratches and rain. And there are plenty of pockets.' He tried another zip and this time managed to make it work. 'This one is particularly useful for balls.' He unzipped a second pocket. 'This one has one special compartment for your sunglasses and another for your mobile telephone. There are eleven pockets altogether, plus an integral tee and ball dispenser, a ball wipe mount and an umbrella station.'

'I could fit a tent in there,' I told him. 'Actually, I don't need a tent. I could just carry the bag round with me and live in it. I've seen mobile homes that are smaller than that.'

He looked at me, not certain whether or not I was trying to be funny.

'And I could get a small stove in that big pocket,' I added.

'Not a bad idea at all,' said the professional who clearly did not have a well-developed sense of humour. 'I know that in the colder weather one or two of the players do carry thermos flasks.'

I lifted the bag. Or, to be more accurate, I tried to lift the bag. Even empty I could hardly move it off the ground.

'You'll need a trolley, of course,' said the professional. 'We have two models. The Penny-Pincher standard economy trolley for the player who doesn't mind other people knowing that he likes to be economical and the Super-Glide for the discerning player who is prepared to pay that little bit extra for real quality.'

'What's the difference?'

'Just quality, appearance, finish and operative functionality. The standard model is designed for the player who is on a tight budget and isn't looking for top level performance. Usually the younger player who doesn't much mind what other members think of him and is prepared to do a little maintenance work on the trolley in the evenings at home.' He poked a finger into his right ear and wiggled it about. He reminded me of a cat scratching itself. 'No point in skimping to my mind,' he said. 'If I had saved money when I had some money I still wouldn't have any now because I would have used it as soon as I hadn't got any which was a long time ago. What's the stuff for anyway? If you don't spend it what's it for?'

I didn't understand any of this but, naturally, as a discerning player who was not immune to the sneers and giggles of my fellow man I bought the Super-Glide. It would, I told myself, pay for itself in the long run. Good quality is always worth paying for, I convinced myself, and the study, well-built model would be bound to hold its second-hand value better.

A tall, thin man wearing a clergyman's collar entered the shop and looked around.

'More tees, vicar?' asked Walter.

'If you'd be so kind,' replied the clergyman. He took a packet of tees from the professional, handed him some coins and left without another word.

'That's the vicar,' explained Walter. 'Nice chap. Never loses balls – he's still using the same ball he had when he started playing eleven years ago – but he gets through two packets of tees a week. Don't know what the dickens he does with them.'

'Do you have lots of professional men playing golf?' I asked.

'Oh yes. Clergymen. Doctors. Undertakers. We've got them all here. All the quality people. I heard a rumour today that we've got a plumber joining. Don't see many plumbers these days, do you?'

'No. I guess not,' I muttered.

'You'll need clothes, of course,' said the professional.

'Oh, I've got plenty of clothes,' I assured him, confidently. 'I'm sure I can find something suitable for stumbling around in a field.' I was, I confess, thinking of a pair of old brown corduroy trousers and a battered green Barbour jacket. It had occurred to me that dressed thus I might be able to make my way around the course without being noticed. I have always rather favoured the inconspicuous style when choosing clothes.

The professional glowered at me and said nothing but said it with tremendous venom.

I swallowed, smiled nervously and shrugged as if this had been just another small attempt at humour.

The professional continued to say nothing.

'Maybe if you've got something in my size that you think would be suitable?' I suggested.

'If you look the part, you'll play the part,' Walter said. He seemed to have learned by heart quite a number of slick advertising phrases. He reached up and pulled an item of clothing from a rack behind him. 'You'll want three of these,' he told me. The item of clothing he had selected was difficult to classify at first meeting but my initial impression was that it was intended to be a cross between a shirt and jumper. I took the thing from him. It had short sleeves, a curious little roll collar and three buttons. The body and sleeves of the thing were pink but the frontal chest area was decorated with green triangles. Each triangle was picked out with a cream surround. There was a large yellow elephant sewn into the shirt just above the left nipple and the word 'Plug' embroidered just above the right. The elephant had blue eyes and a huge sickly smile which made him look as though he was about to be sick. It was the brother (or the sister) of the garment which adorned the professional's own torso.

'You think this is the bee's knees, eh?' I asked.

'Made by Tittery in 100% pure acrylic and designed and endorsed by Plug Bashing,' said the professional.

'Is that good?' I asked.

'Plug Bashing was ninth in the Open seven years ago,' said Walter, as though this put questions about his design skills out of play. 'Or maybe it was seventh in the Open nine years ago.'

'Do I need to try one of these on?'

'They're all the same size,' said the professional. 'It's some special stretchy material. I think they make it out of nuclear waste. The clothes fit anyone. It solves stock problems.'

'Right,' I nodded. 'That's good.'

'They're coated with water repellent silicone,' continued Walter. 'Guaranteed to provide 75% protection against 2,000 litres of rain an hour falling at 15 mph for the first 30 minutes and then 50% protection against 1,000 litres of rain an hour falling at 7.5 mph for the second 30 minutes.'

'Crumbs.'

'After that you'll need an umbrella.'

'Ah.'

The professional took a large pink umbrella from a chimney pot which was serving as an umbrella stand. 'These are the ones we recommend.'

'Why do you recommend those?'

'They're the only ones we sell. They're made by the same people who make the sweaters.'

'Right,' I said.

'And you'll need the trousers to match.'

'To match the umbrella?'

'The sports shirt,' said Walter.

I looked at the sweater and then at Walter. 'There are trousers which go with it?' I asked. The irony was wasted. The professional opened a drawer, rummaged around for a moment, and then tossed not one but three polythene bags onto the growing pile. 'Matching trousers,' he said. 'You'll need three pairs.' It was clear that each bag contained something which could, broadly speaking, be described as clothing. Since the clothing was coloured pink and was decorated with the same triangular motif it was impossible to deny that, whatever it was, it matched the other thing. I ripped one of the polythene bags and opened out a pair of pink trousers. The word 'Plug' was printed on one back pocket and an image of a yellow elephant on the other. The elephant was grinning and I was beginning to suspect that he was grinning at me.

'Why do I need three of everything?' I asked Walter.

'One in the wash, one to wear and one to replace the pair that gets taken by mistake in the clubhouse.'

'Stolen?'

'These are very popular but they fit anyone. People pick up the wrong ones.'

'I could take theirs if they fit everyone.'

Walter ignored this. 'And we have a special offer on this year,' he went on. 'If you buy two you pay for three so we give you the third pair free.'

'Should I try them on?' I asked.

The professional shrugged. 'You don't need to,' he said. 'They only make the one size.'

I looked at him.

'Elasticated waist,' he explained. 'Brilliant. Fit a broom handle or a whale.'

'Wonderful.' I agreed.

'You'll need gloves,' said the professional. He took several packets from an open cardboard box on his desk and tossed them casually onto the growing pile of equipment now making a small mountain on the floor of his prefabricated shop.

'Oh, I don't think we need bother about those,' I said, with a timid laugh as hollow as a politician's promise . 'I never wear gloves. I'm blessed with marvellous circulation.'

'These are for grip,' said the professional tersely. 'You can't play golf without gloves.'

I picked up one of the packets. The glove inside looked like a rather thin driving glove, except that it was made of light blue leather and was decorated with an embroidered likeness of the now familiar elephant. I opened the packet and took out the contents.

'There's only one glove,' I said, peering inside the empty packet. 'Either there's been a mistake or these were made for one armed golfers.'

'You only wear one on your left hand,' said the professional.

'Why?' I asked, slipping the glove on. It felt very tight.

'Because they only make a glove for the left hand.'

'What do left handers wear?'

'A right-handed glove.'

'Could I have one of those as well? Then I can wear a pair.'

'We don't have any. We tell left handers to wear the glove turned the other way round.'

I removed the glove and put it onto my right hand. The elephant was now nestling in my palm. 'Like this?' I tried to flex my fingers. It was very difficult.

'Like that. The embroidered elephant on the palm gives extra grip.'

'So why don't they put the embroidered elephant on the palm of the left hand glove?'

'They like to give left handers a bit of an edge. Their being left handed.'

'You don't have the gloves in pink, I suppose?' I asked. 'To match everything else?'

'No. I ran out of pink gloves four years ago, shortly after they discontinued the Plug Bashing range.'

'They discontinued it?'

The professional shrugged.

I looked disconsolately at the enormous pile of Plug Bashing clothing I was buying.

'Anyway,' continued Walter, 'you don't want everything matching. You'd look a bit of a plonker, wouldn't you?'

There seemed some sense in what he said, though I was surprised that he was the one who said it.

'Balls?'

'I beg your pardon?'

'You'll need a lot of balls?'

'To wear these trousers?' I asked.

Walter ignored this. 'We've got several sorts,' he said, waving a hand around. 'But economising on balls is always a big mistake.' He reached behind him and produced a cardboard tube. 'Three of the very best money can buy,' he said. 'And only £1 a ball more than some of the cheaper ones.'

'What's the difference between the cheaper ball and the more expensive one?'

'A pound. I've just told you.'

'Right. How many do you think I'll need? One? Two?'

'Oh, two dozen should be fine for starters. You can always come back for more.'

'Two dozen?' I exclaimed.

'Yes. You're right. Bit skimpy. Better make it three dozen.' He took several packs of balls from the display and piled them high on the counter. 'You'll want shoes too, of course. You can't play golf in ordinary shoes.'

'I can't?'

'Of course not.'

'Why not?'

'No grip.'

'Oh.'

'And the club doesn't allow members onto the course unless they're wearing proper footwear.'

'So what counts as proper footwear?'

'The sort of shoes we sell.'

'Do you have anything in my size? Eleven.'

He opened a drawer and rummaged around among a pile of white shoe boxes. 'I've got a ten or a twelve in the Sam Hogan Professional Range.'

'Who was Sam Hogan?' I asked. 'I've heard of someone called Ben Hogan. But who was Sam?'

'I think he may have been a relative,' said the professional. 'He was less well known. If you buy a shoe endorsed by a professional you have to pay extra. So it makes sense to buy something endorsed by a professional who isn't going to charge too much.'

I agreed that this made a certain amount of sense. The shoes were two-tone correspondent shoes. Brown and white.

'Do you want the ten or the twelve?'

'A ten will be too tight.'

'My feeling exactly. The twelve will be better. You'll be wearing thick golf socks anyway. So an eleven would probably be too small.'

'Shall I try them on?'

Grudgingly, he took the shoes from the box. I tried one on. It was a big twelve. I think I could have got both feet in the one shoe.

'Perfect,' he told me, peering down at my feet. I stuck my fingers down the back of the shoe. 'They're a bit on the spacious side,' I complained.

'Nonsense. The feet always swell up when you're playing golf. You'll need plenty of room. We always recommend that our customers buy a bigger size than normal.'

'Oh.'

'How many pairs of golf socks would you like?'

'Do I really need special socks?'

'Oh yes.'

'What's the difference between golf socks and ordinary socks?'

'Golf socks have specially reinforced heel and toe supports. To provide extra protection and double the friction when you're swinging the club. Proper golf socks can make a huge difference to your accuracy and distance off the tee. You won't see the professionals playing in ordinary socks.'

'So if I wear these I'll play better?'

'Definitely. Guaranteed.'

I hesitated.

'And they have a little golfing motif at ankle height,' said Walter. 'Tasteful but distinctive.'

I put my foot down firmly and bought just two pairs.

'Cheque or credit card?' the professional asked, when he'd finished adding up my bill.

'Card,' I said, taking out my wallet and extracting a credit card.

'Shall I put you down for insurance too?'

'Insurance?'

'In case you lose your clubs, hit someone with a ball or score a hole in one.'

I stared at him. 'Why would I need insurance if I scored a hole in one.'

'You'd be expected to buy a drink for everyone in the clubhouse. It can get very expensive.'

'And in case I hit someone?'

'I read just the other day of a golfer who hit a sliced three iron and hit a hiker on the head. The hiker overbalanced and fell off a cliff. His widow sued for £7.6 million damages. I hate to think what the legal costs added up to. Unless you're the sort of chap who regards £7.6 million as small change I would seriously consider the insurance.'

I paled. I hadn't thought of golf in those terms. It had never occurred to me that a game might leave me bankrupt.

'The standard policy costs just £5 though I feel the cover is rather limited.'

'Limited?'

'To a maximum of £5,000 for any one incident.'

'So if I hit a hiker on the head and he fell off a cliff I'd have to find the other £7,595,000 myself?'

'Unless you took out the optional super enhancement cover.'

'How much is that?'

'£99 a year for full replacement of your clubs if they are stolen, £1,000 if you score a hole in one in a tournament and up to £250,000 public liability damages.'

'I'd still have to find the other £7,350,000 myself if I hit a hiker on the head?'

'Well, you can't expect the insurance company to take all the risk,' said the professional. 'They don't want to feel that golfers are out there willy nilly knocking balls about without looking out for hikers.'

'I suppose not,' I agreed. I handed him my credit card.

The professional filled in a credit card slip and ran my card through the machine. He handed me the slip to sign. I signed it without looking at it, not because I am reckless with money but because I am easily scared.

'Now, I expect you'll want to book some lessons. What time of day do you prefer?'

Chapter Five

'Hello. I'm Not A Plumber.'

'How much did he take you for?' asked Simon.

'Who?' I asked.

Simon looked at me, and then at the two black refuse sacks beside me. The professional didn't have any plastic bags so he had put the clothing I'd bought into bin liners. The clubs, the bag, the balls, the gloves and the trolley were all packed into the boot of my car. They took up so much room that at one point I had thought I might have to jettison the spare tyre. The packet of golf tees was in my pocket. Because Walter hadn't charged me for them he hadn't put them in with the other items.

I pulled the credit card slip out of my pocket and handed it over. I didn't have the courage to look at it myself.

Simon whistled.

'Bad?' I asked him.

'You went for the full Monty didn't you? Did you buy the golf socks too?'

'Yes.' I whispered, rather embarrassed at my gullibility.

'With the reinforced toe and heel sections to improve ball striking and give you more accuracy and distance off the tee?'

'Those were the ones,' I whispered. 'Though it was the golf orientated motif on the ankles which really got me.'

'How many pairs?'

'Two.'

'You did better than me. I bought three pairs.'

'Do they make any difference?'

Simon looked at me and raised an eyebrow but said nothing.

'Sorry,' I apologised. 'I was still sort of...hoping.'

'Did you buy an elbow restraint?'

'A what?'

'It's a sort of cross between an elastic bandage and a drainpipe. You're supposed to wear it when you're practising; to keep your elbow in the right position. He didn't try and sell you one?'

I shook my head.

'He used to claim he swore by it when he was a professional. He'll probably get you later with that one. Have you booked lessons?'

I said I had.

'Ah,' said Simon. 'He'll get you then. Did he tell you about his days of glory? His memory has pretty much gone – at least he can never remember who I am and as far as I know he can never remember who anyone else is – but he can remember every shot he played forty years ago.'

'He told me he used to play on the professional tour. He said he nearly won the Open.'

'Indeed, I believe he nearly did. Did he specify the variety of Open which he nearly won?'

'No. Is there more than one type?'

'Oh, there are many varieties of Open. The one that Walter nearly won was the Midland Junior Open Championship. He led for two rounds and then blew up and came last.'

'He said he came sixth.'

'He did. There were only six competitors.'

'Ah.'

'Maybe he's run out of the elbow restraints. I think they stopped making them in 1958. Pity. I kept meaning to buy one or two and tuck them away in the loft. There's a huge market in golfing memorabilia these days. I'm sure that elbow restraints will have their day in the auction rooms. Did he offer you a discount?'

'I did get a discount on some of my clubs.' I said. 'Though I think he forgot to apply it to the rest of the bill.'

'Member's discount?'

'Yes.'

'One per cent?'

'Yes. But the way he worked it out I don't think it was that much.'

'It never is. I once bought three second-hand golf balls from him. They were 50 pence each. He used a calculator to add up the cost and deduct my discount and then charged me £3.47. I was on the 4th green before I realised I'd been done.'

'I got free tees.'

Simon looked at me.

'Honestly. With the clubs.'

'Free tees?'

'Yes.'

'New ones? Not the broken halves you find lying around all over the first few yards of every hole on the course?'

'Still in the packet. A bit sun faded and the price on the packet is marked in shillings and pence. But they're still in the packet so as far as I'm concerned they're new.'

Simon held out a hand. I took it. 'Congratulations,' he said. 'I don't know anyone who's ever got anything free out of our professional before. Back in the days when he knew who I was, I ran into him in the car park outside the library. He told me he'd spotted me out on the course and thought I was dropping my right shoulder too much on my back swing. I thanked him and thought what a decent egg he was. The next time I got to the course I found a brown envelope in my locker. It contained an invoice for £27 for 'Advice pertaining to golf matters.'

'I'll remember that if I see him around town,' I said.

'Did you meet his assistant?'

'Didn't know he'd got one.'

'Name of Vincent. Cocky bastard. Short, dumpy fellow. He's going bald so he shaves his head to disguise the fact but you can still see where the hair is growing and where it isn't. He's always talking about the job here just being temporary until he gets his tour card but he's been 29 for as long as I can remember and he's as far away from a tour card as I am. He likes to be called Hippo.'

'Hippo?'

'Hippo. He's a bit overweight and so he says he's a hippo not a tiger. He says having a nickname will help him get publicity when he starts winning tournaments.'

'I'll look out for him.'

'Don't bother. He's hardly ever around. I haven't seen him for a year. Did you really get free tees?'

'Definitely.'

'Could I see them?'

I took the tees out of my pocket and handed them to him.

'You're right,' said Simon, handling the tees as though they were a holy relic. 'These are brand new. Circa 1965 but brand new. You're the first person I've ever known to get something for free from Walter. You're not a lawyer are you?'

'No.'

'Oh, no of course not,' said Simon, remembering. 'You're a plumber, aren't you?'

'No.'

'You're not a plumber?'

'Afraid not.'

'So what do you really do?'

'I'm a journalist. I edit the local free paper.'

'That darned thing that gets delivered every Thursday by a snotty little kid who rides over my lawn on his bicycle?'

'That's the one.'

'Full of house ads, car ads and leaflets for the local supermarket?'

I nodded.

'You edit the bits of stuff between the adverts?'

'I write most of it too.'

'Under your own name?'

'Oh no. I'm Dirk when I write the news reports, Ali and Samantha for features, Arthur when I do the gardening, Thelma for the village reports, Gracie for the kids page, Edith for the woman's page, Rick for the music page and Felicity when I do the arts page.'

'You can't stop that snotty little kid delivering the damned thing can you?'

I laughed.

'I don't mean to be rude but since they introduced the new

weekly limits on rubbish we've been pushed to get all our rubbish into two black sacks. Your paper takes up a quarter of a sack every week.'

'Don't you have a cat?'

Simon looked puzzled.

'A lot of people tell me they find it useful as a litter tray lining.'

'I suppose we could get a cat,' he said thoughtfully. He thought for a moment. 'But that would mean more rubbish, wouldn't it?'

'What do you do?' I asked him.

There was a pause. 'I used to tell people that I was an IT consultant,' said Simon. 'But then people asked me to sort out their computers so I've given that up. Until I think of something better and safer the truth is that I've got a stationery shop in the High Street. I inherited it from my father. Pens, pencils, paper – that sort of stuff. It's pretty low grade information technology but it's still information technology stuff. The highest tech item we sell is a pencil with a rubber glued on the end of it.' He grinned. 'Actually, before computers came along it used to be a good little business. Not today though. We're slowly going bust but there's nothing we can do about it.'

'Why are you going bust?'

'Too much competition. A few years ago I thought we would go bust because everyone would have a paperless office. Got that wrong. More paper around than ever. But the computer did for us another way. Everyone buys their stationery from the big chains, the mail order suppliers or stores on the Internet. They have computers to control their stock and we can't match the prices the big mail order companies sell at. Some of the stuff we sell we can buy cheaper from the big mail order companies than we can get it from our wholesaler. We just sell stuff to people when they run out and can't wait for next day's delivery. The Council rates go up every year, we've had to spend a fortune putting in a ramp so that we comply with new laws about access for disabled customers, our insurance has tripled in the last five years and our best and most regular customers are shoplifters. Some days the only customers we have are the kids who come in when school finishes and steal pencils. If we didn't own the building and had to pay rent we would make a loss.' He took a deep breath. He looked weary. 'When we stop making a profit I'll sell up and retire. Within ten years this town will consist of nothing but estate agents and charity shops.'

'I'm sorry.'

Simon shrugged. 'It used to worry me but I don't care any more,' he said. 'I've always been the sort of person who is happy to wait for life to come to him. People describe me as 'bland' but I see blandness as a virtue. The world needs more bland people and less people who are convinced that they know exactly what needs to be done to make the world a better place. Meanwhile, we struggle on. I'd sell up and concentrate on my golf – I could be a professional on the tour if I had more time to spare – but who would want to buy a moribund stationery shop?' He looked at me and grinned broadly. 'Actually, come to think of it, if I'd put as much time and effort into the shop as I have into trying to play golf I'd probably be running the biggest stationery business in the world by now.'

* * *

'Been buying tees, have you?'

We both looked up. A tall, thin, elegant man stood beside us. He wore a charcoal grey suit with a thin chalk stripe, an old-fashioned white shirt with a detachable collar and something which looked like a club or regimental tie. He had sunken cheeks, sunken eyes and bony hands with long, exceedingly bony fingers. His hair, completely grey, was parted neatly in the centre. Although he had approached us as silently as a hunter approaching game he had clearly walked with, and now leant heavily upon, a slender black cane which had a silver top and a silver band about six inches below.

'This is Oliver,' said Simon. 'He's one of our oldest and most revered members. And by far and away the best source of local gossip for a hundred miles in any direction. He used to be something important in a bank until they sacked him for being senile.'

'What are you doing sitting here?' he asked, ignoring Simon's introduction.

'What's wrong with here?' asked Simon.

'Too far from headquarters,' said Oliver, nodding in the direction of the gent's. 'A professional drinker should always have a table near headquarters. It's just plain silly to waste time walking to and fro.'

'It's nice here,' said Simon. 'Besides, walking to the loo keeps me fit.'

'Good thought,' agreed Oliver. He looked around. Maybe we should make this our new HQ.' He slumped down in the chair next to me. 'So, you're the new member,' he said. He smiled at me, examined me over the top of a pair of expensive-looking half moon gold-framed spectacles, and eagerly shuffled forward in his chair. 'Plumber, I understand? I wonder if you could pop round to my place sometime? Devil of a game getting hold of one of you fellows these days. I spent three days waiting for one to call the other week. He kept saying he'd come but he never appeared. It was like waiting for Godot but less rewarding. I've got a tap that's been dripping for years. And two of my radiators don't work. Do you do heating as well? It's all pipes isn't it?'

A second newcomer, shorter, rounder and altogether quite different to Oliver, wandered over carrying a large cigar from which he was carefully removing the cellophane wrapper. He was about nine inches too short for his weight and four inches too stout for his trousers.

'I'm not actually a plumber,' I told Oliver, determined to scotch the rumour.

'This is Gerald,' said Simon, introducing me to the cigar smoker.

'Hello. I'm not a plumber,' I said, shaking his hand.

'Neither am I,' he replied. 'I wonder what else we've got in common?'

Oliver looked resigned rather than disappointed. 'Can't believe anything anyone tells you these days,' he complained, more in sadness than despair. 'Pork pies,' he muttered. 'Everyone tells you pork pies these days.'

'Pork pie?' said Gerald, overhearing and misinterpreting what Oliver had said. 'Damned good idea. Haven't eaten for decades. Anyone else peckish?'

'Sounds good,' agreed Simon. He looked at me. 'They serve a good pie here,' he promised me.

'Sounds good to me,' I agreed.

'Oliver?' asked the man with the cigar.

'Tell that damned idiot behind the bar to give me plenty of pickle. Can't eat pork pie without lashings of pickle. And don't put any water in my whisky. If I want to drink water I'll go swimming.'

Gerald screwed up the cellophane from his cigar and tried to put it into the ashtray on our table but the cellophane refused to stay screwed up. 'To Oliver, a water-hazard is someone being heavy-handed with a water jug,' he said.

'Why did they tell me you're a plumber when you're not?' Oliver asked. He stared at me. 'Are you sure you're not a plumber?'

'Pretty sure.'

Gerald took a gold lighter out of his waistcoat pocket and set fire to the cellophane. The cellophane burnt fiercely for a moment before disappearing. 'Drinks all round?' he asked us. We all nodded. 'What are you drinking?' We told him and he tottered off in the direction of the bar.

Oliver sighed. 'Pity. I wish I'd been a plumber. I would have made a fortune and got all those earthy housewives thrown in free too.'

'Earthy housewives?' demanded Simon, who had nodded off but been awoken by this. 'What on earth are you talking about, Oliver?'

'Housewives,' said Oliver, raising his voice as though talking to a foreigner who didn't speak very good English. 'They sit around all day with nothing to do and when the plumber calls they feed him tea and cakes and then leap on him for afters.'

A young woman in a blue trouser suit who was sitting at a nearby table turned and scowled at us.

'So, if you're not a plumber, what do you do?' asked Oliver, either unaware of the disapproval or unconcerned by it.

I told him.

'Can't trust the damned newspapers these days,' said Oliver. 'Journalists just sit in the office and make it all up. Do you do that?'

'Not always,' I laughed.

'You just hire someone to slip in deliberate mistakes to confuse people like me?'

'How did you find out?' I asked.

Oliver slapped his knee. 'There you are!' he said, addressing Simon. 'I knew that was what the buggers did.'

* * *

The pork pie was good. There was plenty of pickle. We ate well. It was dark when Simon and I said 'goodbye' to Gerald and Oliver. As we left the clubhouse we bumped into two people. The first was Walter, the golf professional. We both said hello.

He stared at us, frowning. 'Do I know you?' he demanded.

'We're members,' said Simon.

'I was in your shop earlier,' I told him.

'Did you buy anything?' he asked. He reminded me of my headmaster.

'Full set of clubs, a bag, trolley and two sacks full of golf clothing,' I told him.

He beamed. 'Good chap,' he said. 'Well done.' He patted me on the head, like a headmaster attempting to show a previously unseen benevolent side to a junior boy. I felt as though I was being congratulated on some minor achievement. Walter then disappeared, ignoring Simon completely.

The second person we ran into was a harassed looking man in a blue boiler suit. He was carrying a black briefcase and a clipboard. The words 'Consultant Plumbing Engineer' were embroidered above one of the breast pockets of his boiler suit.

'Excuse me,' he said. 'Someone called for a plumber. Sorry I'm late. I got called away. Crisis.'

'Oh dear,' said Simon. 'Big leak somewhere?'

'No. My daughter's hamster died. She found it dead at the bottom of the cage. I had to go home and bury it and then go out and buy her a new one. My wife was in a terrible state. She was very attached to that hamster.'

'Well I think our problem here has been sorted now,' said Simon.

'Oh. Right. Sorry about that,' said the plumber. He turned and headed back to a large white van.

Simon looked at me. 'Bugger it,' he said. He grinned broadly. 'You really aren't a plumber, are you?' He suddenly started after the plumber. 'Excuse me!' he called. 'Just wait a minute, please!'

The plumber, who was about to climb into his van, stopped and turned.

'I say,' I heard Simon say. 'Could you pop round and take a look at a tap in our bathroom? Damned thing has been dripping...' The plumber opened his briefcase and took out a huge blue diary.

I waved and headed for my car. Simon, grinning hugely, waved back and held up a thumb.

Chapter Six

'They're Clubs Not Sticks.'

My first golf lesson took place at 6pm the following evening.

'Hmmph,' said Walter, staring at me as though he thought he might have seen me somewhere before but couldn't quite place me. He was carrying a golf club and using it as a walking stick; holding the business end of the club as a handle and sticking the top of the handle into the ground as he leant on it. 'I thought we'd do some bunker practice this evening.'

'Right,' said I. 'Let battle commence. Which stick do I need for that?' I had, in honour of the occasion, dressed entirely in the clothes I'd bought from Walter's shop. I was a veritable bouquet of yellow and pink. Small elephants blossomed about my person. I may have been destined for disappointment when the list of the world's best dressed men was published but I felt I would hold my own on a list for golfers making an effort to look like golfers. My bag, stuffed with spare balls, spare clothing and, lest the lesson stretch too long into the night, several packets of sandwiches, two thermos flasks (one containing coffee and one containing soup), two bottles of mineral water, two cans of lager and three bananas, rested waiting on my brand new trolley. Preparing the bag, and working out how to strap it onto the trolley, had taken me the best part of the afternoon. Having pushed the trolley from the car park to the practice ground, where the lesson was being held, I was exhausted and rather thought I might be the first golfer in history to need a caddy to push my trolley round the course for me.

'That one!' said Walter, pointing to one of my clubs with the handle of his stand-in walking stick. 'And they're clubs not sticks,' he snarled.

I plucked the chosen club from the bag, took hold of it with both hands and started to wave it about.

'Where the hell did you learn that grip?' demanded Walter, stepping back two paces. I was not sure whether this was because he was physically fearful for his safety or because he was so shocked by what he saw that he needed to distance himself from it.

'What grip?' I asked, looking down at the club I was holding.

'You're holding it like a tennis racquet,' complained Walter.

'Am I?' I was surprised by this and looked down in order to take note of how I was holding the club. I've never played tennis and didn't have the faintest idea how a racquet should be held. I thought that if I could remember the grip I was using it might prove useful one day.

'How many lessons have you had now?'

'This is my first,' I admitted.

'Then what are you doing with that club?' demanded Walter rather crossly. He had fierce eyes and huge black eyebrows like hairy caterpillars and when he was cross the caterpillars shot inwards and joined up. It looked as though the two creatures were mating. Walter lifted his impromptu walking stick and tapped it against another of the clubs in my laden bag. 'Use that one.'

I put the club I was holding back into the bag and pulled out the one chosen to replace it. Walter then proceeded to try to teach me how to hold the club, how to stand and how to swing. He seemed particularly anxious to teach me something called the Vardon grip named, not surprisingly after someone called Vardon. Walter was very keen on Vardon whose grip turned out to be a way of using two hands to hold a golf club. I found it difficult to see why a man who had taught the world how to do this deserved to be immortalised. There is not, as far as a I know, a Grace grip for holding a cricket bat or a Perry grip for the tennis racquet. Offering immortality to a man who has devised a way to use two hands to hold a stick with a lump of metal at the end of it seems like hero worship taken a step too far. It occurred to me (but I did not say) that the man who had worked out how to knot a necktie was perhaps more deserving of this sort of lasting recognition.

In between deifying Vardon, pushing my elbow sideways, urging my left foot forward and encouraging me to force both hips backwards (I ended up feeling as though I was being trained to dance the Conga) Walter gave me an introductory lecture on course etiquette (never throw clubs if there is another player in front of you, never wear ankle socks with shorts and don't ever walk into the clubhouse wearing golf shoes with spikes were the three pieces of advice which stuck in my mind), a short introductory talk on the rules of the game (never clean your balls unless you're on the green was the only one I remembered) and a pep talk which seemed to owe much both to the American evangelical movement and the sort of spirited exhortational style favoured by the exponents of pyramid selling. 'My motto is A for effort,' said Walter firmly. 'Remember that and you won't stray far from the fairway of golfing endeavour.' After fifty minutes of this I was bored rigid. Although I still hadn't hit a ball I had already acquired two large blisters on the palm of my right hand. Besides, I found it hard to have to take advice on how to dress properly from a man who had sold me a pair of pink trousers decorated with cream-edged green triangles and sporting a yellow elephant on one of the back pockets.

Throughout the lesson Walter had given his watch the sort of attention that a man who is hurrying to catch a train might give his time piece. Suddenly, in the middle of a short lecture on the sartorial importance of having neatly tied shoelaces (Walter favoured a double knot, with all loose ends being exactly the same length) the professional stopped talking and tapped the glass of his watch with a fingernail. 'Time's up,' he announced. 'That'll be £29.95.'

I took out my wallet, counted out three £10 notes and handed them over. They disappeared into the professional's pocket so fast that it looked like the first half of a magic trick and I half expected a rabbit or an egg to appear from behind my left ear. Walter made no effort to hand over the five pence change he owed me but he handed me a box. 'What's this?' I asked. 'Your elbow restraint,' he told me. 'The instructions are on the box.'

'Thank you.'

'It's 39.95,' he said.

'Should I make an appointment for another lesson?' I asked when I'd handed over another £40.

He stared at me as though he was a surveyor and I was a house. 'I don't think so,' he said. 'Not a lot of point.' He walked away, stopped and turned round. 'Come and see me when you decide to sell your clubs,' he said. 'I'll give you 35% of what you paid for them.'

I stared at his back for a few moments, not knowing what to say.

* * *

After unstrapping my bag and stowing that and my trolley in the boot of my car I trotted into the clubhouse to change my clothes. I was willing to wear the pink trousers and all the rest of the stuff on the golf course, if that was what was regarded as appropriate and essential, but I was damned if I was going to drive my car through the town wearing the stuff.

When I was younger my mother always taught me to wear clean underwear in case I was run over and had to be taken to hospital. 'You'd be embarrassed if they took you into casualty with dirty underthings,' she told me and although I had some doubts about how concerned I would have been about my underthings if I had found myself laid out on a hospital trolley with crushed limbs and a fractured skull, I had retained the feeling that embarrassment through the wearing of soiled or inappropriate clothing in a hospital casualty department was one of the worst things that could happen to a fellow. I had a friend who had once been stopped by the police while speeding home from a fancy dress party. He had been wearing a pink taffeta ball gown complete with all the trimmings at the time and he, whose mother had filled him with the same basic fears, told me that his sense of embarrassment far outweighed his fear that he might lose his driving licence or be fined.

There was no one in the changing room, and after I'd changed I left my golfing clothes hanging on a peg (hoping, I confess, that someone might steal them) and wandered into the bar to get a drink and see if I could find something to eat.

Simon, Oliver and Gerald were sitting in three of the leather chairs beside the fire. When I'd bought a slice of pork pie (for me) and four large whiskies (one each) I told them what Walter had said to me.

'It wasn't terribly encouraging,' I admitted. 'I've only had the damned clubs for a day and he's offering me 35% of the purchase price.'

Simon waved a hand as though dismissing all this as nonsense. 'Walter is a useless teacher,' said Simon. 'Ignore him. Oh, by the way, did he sell you an elbow restraint?'

'It's next to my shoes in the locker room,' I told him. '£39.95. It was apparently designed by a NASA space engineer and a professor of orthopaedics.'

'Great,' said Simon. 'Glad you've got one. I wouldn't like to think of you trying to make your way through life without an elbow restraint. Don't wear the damned thing, though. Put it in the attic as part of your pension. Elbow restraints will be all the thing on the Antiques Road Show in 2020.'

'Perhaps I can put the pink trousers and the blue plastic bag in the loft too,' I said. 'I'm going to give the game up anyway. I'm already injured and I haven't hit a ball yet.'

'Back?' said Oliver. 'I'm a martyr to my back.'

'Blisters,' I told him.

'But you said you haven't hit a ball yet?'

'All I did was swing the damned club at blades of grass and learn how to tie my shoelaces properly. Oh and Walter kept telling me to keep my head down. I'm not sure why. Do you know why? Why you have to keep your head down? How are you supposed to see where the ball goes if you keep staring at your feet?'

'I think it's so that you can't see him sneering,' said Simon. 'All professionals sneer. It's what they do best. You really haven't actually hit a ball yet?'

'No. I've got 14 golf clubs, a bag, a trolley, a bag full of balls, a packet of tees, gloves, an entire wardrobe in pink and a pair of specially made correspondent shoes which make me look like a 1930s pimp. But I haven't hit a ball yet.'

'Much more fun when you hit the ball,' said Gerald.

'Just remember to bend your knees,' said Oliver. 'Golf is like skiing. It's all in the knees. You need the flexibility that comes with bent knees.' He paused and thought for a moment. 'But don't bend them too much,' he added. 'Bend them too much and you'll top the ball.'

'Nonsense,' said Gerald. 'Keeping the knees bent is of minor importance. The crucial thing to remember is to keep control of the club. And don't swing back too far. Lots of golfers make the mistake of over-swinging. I never take my club back higher than an imaginary horizontal line drawn backwards from my waist.'

'Don't listen to him,' said Simon. 'I can throw a golf ball further than he drives one.'

'But my drives go straight,' said Gerald. 'When was the last time you played a shot off a fairway? Five years ago? Ten years ago? The club doesn't need to mow the fairways at all for you. We could save a fortune on men and mowers.'

'I'm just going through a bad patch,' protested Simon.

'It's because you're not bending your knees enough,' said Oliver.

'Tell you what, why don't we meet you here tomorrow morning at 10,' said Simon. 'The three of us were going to play together. Why don't you join us?'

Gerald and Oliver murmured their approval of this suggestion. They seemed enthusiastic. I was flattered. I hadn't been playing long enough to know that all golfers like to play with beginners. It gives them a rare chance to play with someone less capable than themselves, and a chance to be in a position to offer advice.

'I'm not sure I should bother carrying on,' I said. 'Walter didn't seem to think there was much point.'

'Walter is a nincompoop,' said Oliver. 'He probably just wanted you to flog him back your clubs – so that he could sell them again as new and make a huge profit.'

'I think he's got brain damage,' said Gerald. 'A few years ago he was hit on the head by a golf ball.'

'Another player's ball hit him?' I asked.

'No. He hit his drive into the trunk of a tree. It bounced back and felled him. He wore a motorcycle crash helmet for six months after it happened.'

'A pal of mine was there,' said Oliver. 'He congratulated old

Walter and asked him how he had managed it and whether he recommended a three wood or a driver for that shot. Walter, who was lying flat on his back, sat up, shook his head and said: 'I believe you know my terms for tuition, Mr Jenkins.' He then fell back and remained unconscious for another fifteen minutes.'

'I suppose you play your ball where it lies when that happens,' said Oliver. 'Bounce off the skull. That sort of thing.'

'Run of the ball,' agreed Simon.

'I bet wearing a crash helmet played havoc with his swing,' I said.

'The ball on the head may have had something to do with his mental condition,' agreed Simon. 'But two bottles of gin a day for twenty years probably haven't helped.'

'True,' agreed Gerald. 'I'm only up to a bottle a day and sometimes I can't remember my wife's name.'

'I don't think you're married,' said Simon.

Gerald stared at him, clearly puzzled. 'Aren't I?' He frowned. 'Are you sure?'

'Didn't she divorce you and go off with a pensions expert from Rotherham?'

'Dammit you're right you know,' said Gerald. He paused, took a packet of cigars from his pocket and removed one. 'She said I ignored her and spent all my time playing golf and drinking.' He lit the cigar. 'Bloody cheek.' He turned to me and grinned. I wasn't sure whether he really had forgotten whether he was still married or not.

Simon turned to me. 'The big question is: Now that you've got all these nice, shiny clubs, do you want to hit some balls and have some fun?'

'What time?' I asked.

'Ten o'clock,' said Oliver. 'Unless that's too early for you?'

'No, that's fine.'

'And please don't wear those horrible pink clothes again,' said Simon with a pained expression. 'They make you look like an American pimp.'

Chapter Seven

'If That Had Gone In, It Would Have Been A Six.'

The four of us stood on the first tee. It was drizzling slightly and the colour of the sky suggested that if there was to be any change in the weather it would be for the worse rather than the better. I was wearing a pair of brown corduroy trousers, a fawn jumper and an old leather bomber jacket with an elasticated waist. Of the expensive gear Gerald had sold me I wore only the socks. I still wanted to believe they would help my game and I didn't think anyone else would notice my wearing them. My three companions, who were busy taking out balls, putting on golf gloves and finding tees, were all wearing waterproof jackets and waterproof trousers. Oliver wore a blue woolly hat with a picture of a skier on the front, Gerald wore a baseball cap which suggested that he supported a team playing out of New York and Simon had the hood of his jacket pulled up over his head. 'The thing about drizzle,' said Gerald, 'is that it gets you wet before you realise quite what's happening. By the time you've realised that you're getting wet and you need to wear your waterproofs you're soaked.'

Some golfers never talk while playing, preferring to concentrate on the next shot. Others talk about the game they are playing (or the games they have played with other people) while the third, and by far the largest group, talk about anything but golf. Investments, wives and illnesses are the favourite topics when men golfers talk. (I am reliably informed that women golfers who are married talk mainly about their children, their husbands and their hairdressers.

Women golfers who are single talk almost exclusively about golf.)

'Had to go into hospital yesterday to have me prostate fiddled with,' said Oliver. 'Haven't been to hospital for years. Curious thing, though, the damned places don't smell like they used to. They used to smell of antiseptic. These days they smell of photocopier ink.'

'I hate hospitals,' said Gerald, examining a small hole in the palm of the golf glove he had just pulled on. 'Dunno why but they always remind me of sickness and death. Last time I was in one visiting my sister-in-law I felt queasy. Thought I was having a heart attack. I got my brother to take me home.'

'Hospital is the last place you want to be when you don't feel well,' said Oliver. 'You need to be on top form to survive one of those places.' He shivered. 'Have you noticed that the nurses wear trousers these days?' he asked. He shook his head in disgust.

'The nurses used to make hospitals almost bearable,' said Gerald. 'Short skirts. Starched uniforms. Black stockings...' He gazed dreamily into the far distance, as though attempting to recapture some fleeting memory of a year long gone by.

'This is a par four,' Simon told me, taking a leather cover off the head of one of his clubs. '390 yards. Slight dog leg to the left, as you can see. Watch the trees on the right. There's a stagnant pond hidden just behind them.'

'When they bent over to tuck in the sheets of the bed across the ward you could see their stocking tops,' said Gerald. 'And a few inches of white thigh. Magical.' He sighed. 'Did a man far more good than the damned pills they dole out.'

'It's amazing that with just four hits one can knock a small ball all that way and get it into a metal cup,' I said.

Simon looked at me. 'It certainly is,' he agreed. 'I nearly did it once.'

My three good companions drove off first. They seemed to know the order in which they should start. Simon hit what looked to me to be a perfect drive but, apparently disgusted with himself, he banged his club head on the ground and growled something incomprehensible. Gerald's shot started well but, in mid flight, mysteriously started to curl to the left. It ended up disappearing into a patch of thick grass just to the left of a large bunker.

'Distance isn't everything,' he said.

'True,' said Simon, grinning at him. 'The rough is much thicker further up. You did well to hold that ball back.'

Oliver's drive, though it hardly rose into the air at all, bounced and rolled and skidded and jumped and, much to my surprise, ended up straighter and further than either of the other two balls.

Then it was my turn.

'This is Tom's first ever golf shot,' Simon said to the others. There were murmurings of encouragement. They all kept very still and watched me intently.

My first three shots could comfortably be described as frustrating and insubstantial rather than memorable. Although I gripped the club very tightly and swung it as fast as I could I missed the ball completely on all three occasions.

'Don't worry about it,' said Gerald. 'Think of each shot as a new adventure. Everything starts afresh.'

'Don't try and hit it so hard,' suggested Simon. 'Just stroke it.'

'Just relax,' said Oliver. 'If every golf shot was perfect the game would be very boring. And don't think about it too much. Never let your brain get in the way.'

I could see the sense in all this and so on the fourth attempt I contented myself with a half swing and a gentle follow through. The result, although hardly spectacular, was considerably more successful than its three predecessors. My ball bounced on what I shortly afterwards discovered was the ladies' tee, hit a small notice warning members not to take their trolleys onto the greens, and ricocheted off into the medium length grass just to the right of the fairway. The ball had, I suppose, travelled a total of about sixty yards.

It was not the sort of beginning that would give my golfing biographers much to enthuse about but the club had collided with the ball and it was, therefore, my first real golfing stroke. My first recorded golf shot. My career as a golfer had started.

As I started the short journey from the tee to my ball I felt sure that I caught a glimpse of someone watching me from behind a nearby bunch of bushes. But when I looked harder I could see no one.

* * *

Many golfers report that their first round of golf is their most successful for some time. A grocer I once met told me that it took him four years of practice to achieve a score which matched his very first outing.

This was not my experience.

By the tenth hole I had run out of spare balls and I had borrowed so many from the other three that they had only the balls they were playing with. I was astonished to find out just how easy it was to lose golf balls. On several occasions the ball I hit seemed to trickle off the tee but proved elusive when four pairs of eyes started searching for it.

'This is embarrassing,' I said, balancing my only ball on a red plastic tee I'd borrowed from Oliver. My own supply of tees had long since run out, partly because the ones Walter had given me had turned out to be particularly fragile, and partly because when you tee up at least three times on each hole you are likely to get through three times as many tees as golfers who drive just once. 'If I lose this one I'll just walk back with you. You three must be fed up to the back teeth of playing with such a complete rabbit.'

'Don't be daft,' said Simon. 'This is your first round of golf. You can't give up half way round.' He bent down, unzipped one of the pockets on his golf bag and took out a mobile telephone. 'We like playing with you,' he continued. 'Because you've spent a fortune on all that equipment and you're absolutely crap at golf it makes us all feel good about our own games. Besides, you're rather missing the point, we're not good golfers and none of us want to be good golfers. We enjoy our golf and we know that if we become good at the game all the fun would disappear.'

I must have looked as puzzled as I felt.

'If you're a good golfer,' he explained, 'then the good shots will be routine and the bad shots will be disappointing. Right?'

I thought about this for a moment. 'Yes, I suppose so,' I agreed.

'But if you're a bad golfer then bad shots are routine and only to be expected.'

I nodded.

'Whereas the good shots will be exciting.'

'I think I see what you're getting at,' I said.

'It's much better to be a bad golfer because you get occasional bursts of excitement. Good golfers merely get occasional bursts of disappointment.'

'I hadn't thought of it that way,' I agreed.

He shrugged and smiled. 'Besides,' he continued. 'We get more value for money.'

I looked at him.

'We get to play a hell of a lot more shots per round than a good golfer,' he explained. 'Really good golfers only hit the ball three or four times a hole. Where's the fun in that?'

He punched a number into his mobile phone and held the device up to his ear. He was on the phone for no more than a minute or two. I didn't hear what he said.

'Sorted,' he told me, with a big grin. 'Just try and make that ball last another five minutes and we should be OK.'

Not knowing quite how he had managed to solve my problem with a single phone call when we were at least a couple of miles away from the only known local supply of golf balls I pulled a club out of my bag. Any club. It didn't seem to make any difference which club I played with – all my shots were terrible. My best chance of not losing a ball was to miss the ball completely and hope that the draft made by the club swishing by was not strong enough to waft the ball into an invisible rabbit hole.

'Is there a second-hand market for clubs?' I asked.

'I always blame my clubs when I play badly,' said Gerald.

'Are you going to buy another set already?' asked Oliver. 'You haven't got those dirty yet.'

I sighed wearily. 'No, I think I'm going to give up,' I said.

'Don't be silly,' said Gerald. 'You can't give up. You've hardly started.'

'I thought golf was supposed to be relaxing,' I complained. 'I find this enormously stressful.'

Gerald looked at me and laughed. 'Who on earth told you that?' he demanded. 'What nonsense. Golf isn't supposed to be relaxing. I go to work to relax. I play golf because I have to.'

'I still intend to give it up,' I insisted.

'You won't,' said Gerald. 'By the time you get to the end of this round you'll be hooked on the game, I promise you. You'll play one shot that will convince you that with a bit of practice you can win the Open. You'll play one shot that any professional would be proud to have played. And then, when you get to the end of the round, you won't be able to wait until you can stand on the first tee and start all over again.'

I looked at him in some surprise and a good deal of disbelief.

'You'll see,' said Gerald, with a broad smile. 'It's damned near impossible to give up golf. There are thousands of instructional books and videos on the market but they all explain how to play the game better. None of them attempt to explain how to give it up.' He looked straight at me and pointed a finger at my chest. 'That's because it's impossible,' he said.

'He's right,' said Simon. 'The biggest addiction problem in the country isn't heroin, marijuana, tobacco or alcohol – it's golf. Why on earth would otherwise sensible, rational people play it if they weren't addicted? It's expensive and frustrating and it leads to bad language and to gambling. Those who fail feel inferior, those who succeed become full of self-aggrandisement.'

'The only way to give it up is to get really good at it,' said Gerald. 'My own long-term ambition is to play well enough to be able to stop playing.'

'Not very likely,' murmured Oliver. He winked at me.

Gerald, Simon and Oliver had, up until that moment, seemed extremely sound sort of fellows; reliable chaps whom anyone could happily trust with his wife or car keys. They had shown no previous signs of dementia. But they had not convinced me that I should carry on playing golf. I would, I decided, put an advert in my own paper and sell the clubs that way. I should be able to get half of what I'd paid for them. And in order to satisfy the demands of my doctor and my mother I'd take up badminton or running. If necessary I would even find a bride and get married. Anything would be better than golf. I'd done my best. I'd tried golf and to be honest I was sick to the back teeth of it. I was soaked to the skin. My feet were sore. My hands were blistered. My shoulders ached. I was cold, fed up and as miserable as I could remember being for years.

To my own surprise, and, I think, the astonishment of my companions, I managed to play the next dozen shots with the same ball. Maybe it was because I was taking more care. Maybe it was because I'd decided to give up the game and didn't care what happened. I was so depressed by my failure to hit anything that resembled a passable golf shot that I pretty much lost interest in what was going on and can remember very little of the first few holes of the homeward nine.

I do remember that on the long 12th Oliver surprised himself, and the rest of us, by reaching the green in four. He would have completed the hole in par if his first putt had gone into the hole. It didn't. Nor did the next two putts.

'I remember when you nearly got a birdie on this hole,' said Gerald, trying to comfort him.

Oliver thought for a moment. 'I didn't though, did I?'

'Not quite,' admitted Gerald. 'You just missed it by three shots. But it was a close thing...'

'I remember it as if it were just yesterday,' said Oliver.

'It was yesterday,' Gerald said.

* * *

On the 13th tee I thought I saw someone spying on us from behind a small clump of trees. Ever since the first tee, when I thought I'd spotted someone watching me from behind a clump of bushes, I'd been half convinced that I was being spied on. And while standing on the 13th tee, waiting for my turn to drive, I was sure that I'd seen a stranger peering at me from between the branches of a large rhododendron bush.

'Can you see someone over there?' I asked Gerald, who was standing next to me. I pointed in the direction of the bush.

'Nothing at all, old chap,' said Gerald, after staring at the bush for 20 or 30 seconds. 'Probably just a hallucination. I get them all the time. A couple of weeks ago I drove down the motorway, past the roadworks that have been there for months, and I was convinced that I saw several of the chaps working quite hard. I was so puzzled that I left the motorway at the next turn off and drove back to have another look. They were all standing around talking and drinking tea, of course. The whole thing was just a hallucination.

Happens a lot when you get older. My doctor says it's the drink but that's just nonsense put out by people who don't approve of alcohol. My old mother had hallucinations for years before she died. She was convinced there were little men living in her telly. She was teetotal. Never touched a drop. Not even at Christmas.'

As we wandered down the fairway on the 14th Gerald was very nearly hit by a golf ball driven by one member of a pair playing behind us.

'Sorry about that!' apologised a red-faced fellow in a blue anorak and jeans. 'You don't mind if we drive through, do you?'

'You really should have shouted fore,' said Simon. 'Your ball nearly hit one of us.'

The man in the blue anorak ignored Simon, grabbed a club from his bag and played on.

'Old farts like you lot shouldn't be allowed on the course,' snarled his playing partner, an aggressive young man carrying a huge bag of clubs. He wore a grubby tee shirt and a pair of jeans cut off just below the knees.

The pair of them hurried on without another word.

'I don't know why they bother,' said Oliver, staring at them sadly. 'It's a game. The idea is to enjoy it, not to get it over with as quickly as possible. Some of them look forward all week to a game of golf but then when they get here they can't get round fast enough; can't wait to get it all over with. Can't understand it.'

'Mind you,' said Gerald, 'if we get stuck behind the four horsewomen I can get a bit edgy.'

'That's true,' agreed Oliver.

'But they are much slower than us,' said Simon. 'Kevin told me that one Saturday last July they took nine hours to complete eighteen holes. He swears that they are so slow that the grass gets cut twice before they finish a round.'

'That was an exceptional day,' said Gerald. 'They had to call the doctor on the 8th because Clarisse fell ill. They thought it was her heart. I don't think they usually take much more than seven hours.'

'Who on earth are the four horsewomen?' I asked.

'The four horsewomen of the Apocalypse,' explained Simon

'are called Elsie, Clarisse, Maud and Daphne – though I can never remember which is which. They're fearsome – hence the collective nickname. Off the golf course they're sweet and dainty but once they start playing they swear and throw clubs with the worst of us. They play every day, whatever the weather. Oliver, can you remember which of the four horsewomen is which?'

'Maud is the ex-headmistress. She's in her early 80s and inherited a fortune from her father who invented the zip, the paper clip or something like that. She never lifts a club above her knees and never hits it more than thirty or forty yards. Elsie is the oldest, she's a couple of years older than Maud, and used to be married to a grocer. She's the only one of the four who has ever been married. She's hard of hearing and he had a speech impediment and it was said to have been a perfect marriage until she secretly bought a hearing aid and found out what he'd been saying about her for years. She divorced him in 1967. She has a son who is an MP. She never hits the ball – even on the green – without taking 24 practice swings. She counts them and says it helps her settle down and play better. Her record round this course is 215. Clarisse used to play hockey for the county. She's in her mid 70s and as strong as an ox. I once saw her throw a three iron into a tree on the 6th. It was up there for months. A couple of pals and I were playing behind them one day and they wouldn't let us through. We decided to skip the 12th, walk ahead and continue from the 13th but Clarisse took umbrage. She threw every club in her bag at us and believe me she can throw clubs far further than she can hit balls. And then there's Daphne. She's quite sweet if you can catch her by herself. She was quite a looker in her youth. She's 78 or 79 I think and she's put on a lot of weight in recent years but when she was young she was a ballet dancer. Not a principal dancer you understand. But a dancer nonetheless. These days she moves slower than a soldier looking for landmines.'

I played the 14th carefully, so as not to lose the ball. I think I took 17 but at one point I got stuck in a bunker and rather lost count.

In my head I'd already drafted the For Sale advertisement I would insert to get rid of my unwanted clubs. *Almost new set of golf clubs for sale. Illness and sudden change in family circumstances forces reluctant sale after one game.'* The newspaper I edit has a free small ad column for people selling stuff under £200. Rather than hang on to the damned things, and be constantly reminded of my unhappy and expensive experience, I would sell them cheap for £199.99 – just inside our price limit. I'd decided I'd rather do that than sell them back to Walter. The whole sorry adventure would have been an expensive lesson but I would, I hoped, learn something from the experience. I would have at least learned that I didn't much like golf. I found an old restaurant receipt and a stub of pencil in my jacket pocket and wrote out my advertisement on the back of the restaurant receipt. I felt much better when I'd done this.

As I stuffed the paper and pencil back into my pocket I heard something that sounded rather like an old steam train rattling towards us at quite a pace.

We had just come down from the fifteenth tee, an elevated position overlooking a long tree-sheltered fairway which I suspect I would, in other circumstances, have found an extremely attractive setting for an afternoon walk on a summer's day. I looked back up the hill but could see nothing. It seemed unlikely that a steam train would have strayed onto the golf course, particularly since closures had ensured that there were not, as far as I was aware, any railway lines within thirty miles.

* * *

Simon hit a wonderful drive and a sequence of poor iron shots. Gerald and Oliver hit slightly wayward drives but hit decent recovery shots which left them near to the green. I hit a poor drive and a series of poor iron shots.

The source of the noise was closer now but it no longer sounded like a steam train. It sounded like nothing I had ever heard before in my life. The only thing I was certain of was that the noise came from somewhere behind us. Oliver and Gerald, who seemed utterly unconcerned and uninterested in the appalling sound made by this approaching monster, were occupied looking for Gerald's ball which had landed in a thick patch of gorse just beside the green. Cries of annoyance and pain alternated as the pair of them struggled amidst the prickles; their waterproofs snagging and tearing with almost every step. I turned round again, listened and looked.

The first thing I saw were rapidly rising puffs of black smoke. It looked as though the cardinals had failed to elect a pope. Or as if a bad-tempered Indian was sending angry messages to a supplier of leaky teepees.

Next, coming over the brow of the hill behind us, I saw what looked like a submarine periscope, then a small wire netting cage and finally a rapidly moving, grass-splattered tractor.

It was impossible to tell what colour the tractor had originally been for now it was covered in a thick, olive green layer of congealed grass cuttings. The tractor was followed by a green cloud and a host of crows and magpies.

As it approached us the tractor slowed, the sound now down to an ear-splitting whine alternating with a deep-throated, phlegmy chug, and finally halted a couple of yards away. The driver and solitary occupant of the wire-enclosed cab, a small, beady-eyed gnome of a man who looked well past retiring age pushed open his wire-covered door and grinned down at us. He had shiny, pink gums but no teeth that I could see. He wore an old fertiliser sack, which had a roughly cut hole in the top for his head and roughly cut holes in the sides for his arms, and a battered, felt trilby which had once been brown but was now stained with grease, oil and grass. He reached down to the floor of the cab and picked up a large, heavy plastic bag, emblazoned with the name of a well-known supermarket. He held the bag out to Simon who took it and, in return, handed up a £20 note. The note disappeared in an instant, the toothless gnome waved a hand, cackled something incomprehensible, slammed his wire-covered door and put the tractor into gear. After turning, the tractor headed back over the hill; belching black smoke and making an ear-splitting racket. Behind the tractor, mowing blades threw out a cloud of finely cut grass. The crows and magpies, which had stood and strutted idly by when the tractor had halted, now took off again in a cloud of their own, following the tractor and the mowing machine and swooping down whenever they spotted something tasty to eat.

'Jake is one of the best golfers in the club,' said Simon, as the tractor disappeared. 'He still holds the club record which he set when he was 22.'

'Does he still play?' I asked.

'Hasn't played for years,' said Simon. 'He gave it up. He said it was too dangerous.'

'He used to get too excited?' I asked, thinking that perhaps Jake had abandoned golf because the stress gave him high blood pressure. 'He thought he might have a heart attack?'

'No, it wasn't that,' said Simon. 'He used to turn into a raging maniac if he played a bad shot. He attacked an opponent with a sand wedge in 1975 and hasn't played since. Nearly killed the fellow I think. Pity. Fantastic player.' He handed me the plastic bag. 'Here you are. This should keep us going to the end of the round.'

I looked inside the bag. It was, as I had by now guessed, full of golf balls.

'How many are there here?' I asked.

Simon shrugged. 'Dunno. Forty? Fifty? I just buy them by the bagful. Jake is one of the groundsmen,' he explained as the tractor disappeared over the brow of the hill. 'He collects the balls he finds and sells them. Buying our own balls back is cheaper than buying new ones from that rogue Walter.'

I reached for my wallet. 'You must let me pay you.'

Simon held up a hand. 'Buy me a drink,' he said. 'The balls are a present.'

I tried again to give him the money but he was adamant. When I rummaged around in the bag I was astonished to spot a ball which I had found on the first hole and then lost on the second just an hour or two earlier. I recognised the ball because in addition to a crescent shaped cut in the casing, which had been the result of a rather poor iron shot by some other golfer equally unencumbered by talent, the ball was marked with two red spots, clearly made by a felt tip pen. There were another two or three balls which I strongly suspected I had lost earlier in the round. Jake, it seemed, was far better at finding lost balls than we were.

* * *

The miracle happened on the 16th hole and I can, without exaggeration, promise that I will treasure the memory of that moment for as long as I am able to treasure anything. If I have a smile on my face when they straighten my club tie and screw down the lid it will be because, right at the end, I was thinking of that moment.

The 16th hole at our club is, at 170 yards, the shortest of the three par threes on the course. The green is slightly uphill and well-guarded. Immediately to the left of the green there are two deep pot bunkers with almost vertical sides. If you drift even further left than the bunkers the ground slopes steeply down into pretty much impenetrable scrubland. The right side of the green is guarded by a huge, old oak tree whose branches reach well out over the green, making it nigh on impossible to drift a ball into the green from that side. The tree stands on a slope where the grass is mostly thick and lush and a ball which hits the top part of the tree usually clatters down into the grass and disappears from view. A narrow, sloping band of closely cut grass of almost glass-like smoothness stands between the trunk of the tree and the right edge of the green.

When I placed my ball on the tee at the start of this hole I had no idea just how important the shot which followed would be. It was, without any exaggeration, a shot which changed my life but when I gripped the leather-bound part of the shaft, wiggled the head of my three iron and told myself yet again to keep my head down and still it was all done more in hope than expectation; more in the belief that even if I couldn't produce a convincing result I could at least try to look convincing. With a plentiful supply of balls I felt free to hit the ball hard, rather than simply trying to make sure I didn't lose it.

The other three had, of course, already driven. Simon's ball was lying in one of the pot bunkers. Oliver's ball was buried in the long grass underneath the oak tree and Gerald's ball, the only one of the three still visible from the tee, was sitting up quite nicely in the middle of the fairway about forty or fifty yards short of the green.

'Put a bit of left to right fade on it,' suggested Oliver, forgetting or ignoring the fact that even if I understood what he was talking about I would have had no idea how to turn the idea into practice.

'You might need a bit of backspin,' said Gerald. Naturally, he gave me no guidance as to how I might bring this about.

Recklessly and uncaring, thinking now only of the fact that the clubhouse was in sight and that my golf clubs would soon be some other poor fool's burden, I took hold of my club and then swung it as though trying to launch my ball into space.

At first I lost sight of the ball. And then I heard Gerald offer a word or two of honest encouragement. (All golfers will offer unlimited praise and encouragement to fellow players who are losing gloriously but who have punctuated an utterly indifferent display with a single shot of majesty. I felt that Gerald's praise was of sterner stuff.)

'Great shot!' he said. And there was neither irony nor envy in his voice.

'Lovely shot!' added Simon.

I peered ahead and managed at last to catch sight of my ball.

It had, through what good fortune I did not know then and certainly do not know now, flown high and almost straight from the tee. When I first caught sight of it the ball was already beginning its descent. It dipped just in time to avoid the branches of the oak tree, landed on the smooth path of grass which lay between the tree and the green, bounced once, hopped forward twice and then, taken by the curve and slope of the bank, drifted slowly down onto the green. The four of us watched, mesmerised, as the ball rolled across the green towards the pin.

'It's going in!' said Gerald, unbelievingly.

'You've got a hole in one,' whispered Oliver.

The ball didn't go in. I didn't get a hole in one. But it did hit the flag-stick, jump up into the air an inch or two and then roll away to end up no more than six or seven feet from the hole.

I have rarely felt as pleased or as proud of myself as I felt then. It was, of course, an outrageous fluke. It was a shot I would not be able to match for a long, long time. But the only thing that really matters in golf is where the ball ends up. The club you use, the beauty of your swing, whether you bend your knees or not, the number of dimples with which the ball is decorated – all these things are irrelevant. The only thing that really, really matters is where the ball finishes at the end of the shot. No professional would have been ashamed of my shot.

And it was my shot. I had held the club and I had hit the ball. Of the four of us my ball was by far the closest of any to the pin.

What a glorious game golf is, I thought to myself. With a little more practice I could perhaps think about entering a few competitions. If I could do it once I could surely do it again. And again.

As we strolled to the green I felt as though I was walking on air. My feet were no longer sore. My shoulders didn't ache. My blisters were still there but they no longer hurt me.

* * *

Gerald was the first to play. He used a wedge. His ball landed on the front of the green, skidded forward and rolled on and on until it went over the back of the green and disappeared out of sight. Oliver played three shots before managing to slash his ball out of the thick grass underneath the oak tree and onto the right edge of the green. And Simon, after four attempts to remove his ball from the bunker, eventually played out backwards. By the time his ball was on the green he had played eight.

'Take your time,' whispered Simon, as I approached my ball. 'Two putts for a par. And watch out – it's a Rock Hudson putt.'

I looked at him, puzzled. 'What's a Rock Hudson putt?'

'Looks straight but isn't,' replied Simon, still speaking softly, as though concerned that if he spoke too loudly my ball might be offended.

'It'll move a little to the right,' said Oliver, who was crouching down behind my ball, trying to read the line. 'Six inches or so.' He stood up and I heard him creak. He sounded like a door that needed oiling.

'More like a foot,' insisted Gerald. 'Probably eighteen inches. There's quite a slope there.'

'Don't hit it too hard,' said Simon. 'Just make sure you get down in two.'

I could feel my heart beating and there was sweat on the palms of both hands. I wiped my hands on my trousers but could do nothing about my thumping heart. Six feet at most. A par. If I got my ball into the hole in two putts I would have completed the hole in three. The number of shots a professional would expect to take.

I bent over the putt and then backed away again. I bent down and looked at the slope of the green. I got up, stood over the ball again and gripped and regripped my putter. My hands felt like huge hams. My arms felt heavy and unresponsive. I knew that the longer I waited the worse things would get. I swung the putter head back, then forward and hit the ball. I knew I'd overhit from the three gasps, long before the ball sailed merrily past the hole without so much as a passing glance.

Three feet.

I had gone three feet past the hole.

I'd been six feet away and instead of hitting the ball six feet I'd hit it nine feet. How bad can you get?

'Play on,' said Gerald. 'Take your time.'

I crouched over my ball again. Gripped, ungripped and gripped again.

'Good luck,' whispered Simon.

I hit the ball.

It rolled forwards. Too quickly again. Too much adrenalin. The ball hit the back of the hole, bounced up into the air, went around the rim of the hole, threatened to spin off across the green and then suddenly lost all momentum and, exhausted, dropped like a stone.

Into the hole.

Three.

Par three.

A par on my first round of golf.

It would be nearly a year before I completed another hole in par. But I didn't know that then. And I certainly didn't care.

* * *

Golf is the only game where the amateurs, the beginners, the high handicappers can play and enjoy the same courses as the top professionals.

How many amateur tennis players get to experience the joy of a game on Wimbledon Centre Court? How many amateur cricketers ever get to play at Lord's?

And yet every day of the week quite ordinary golfers play rounds on the very same turf as Nicklaus, Palmer, Player and the other greats.

If you tried to play tennis with a professional you wouldn't get your racquet anywhere near the ball. Bam. 'I'm ready now.' 'That was it.' 'Oh.'

But I had learned that a quite ordinary golfer will, during the course of a match, almost always play one shot that any professional would have been proud to have played. It had not yet occurred to me that the worse a golfer is the more shots he will be forced to play and the greater, therefore, the chance that one of those shots will, through a combination of circumstances, turn out to be memorable.

'Terrific hole,' said Simon.

'Congratulations!' said Oliver.

'Brilliant!' said Gerald. 'It's a long time since I've seen anyone play that hole better.' He seemed genuinely pleased for me.

'You had my knees shaking over that return putt,' said Oliver. 'But I was impressed with the way you kept your head.'

We walked off the green together and I felt, for the first time, that I was part of the group. I noticed, quite suddenly and to my surprise, that it had stopped raining. I again had a strange feeling that someone was watching me, this time from behind an ash tree. But at that moment I felt more joy, more delight and more intense personal pride and satisfaction than I could ever remember feeling before. I honestly believe that I could not have been prouder if I had won the Open Championship itself.

The real joy in golf comes, of course, not from the accolades of others but from satisfying the self – and creating a memory that will live and brighten the darkest days of winter when storms and snow make the course unplayable, and the even darker days of old age when it is the body which can no longer sustain the search for the next dream.

How, I felt myself wondering, can a man hit a ball just three times and yet propel it with such accuracy. I was prouder of my par than I would have been of a hole in one. If my ball had gone straight into the hole I would have known that it had been a fluke.

I would not have been able to hide this from myself. But a par? Well, that I could believe was a result of skill.

* * *

'It's your honour,' said Simon as I stood on the 17th tee, waiting for one of the others to play.

'You drive first,' explained Gerald, when I still didn't move. 'You won the last hole.'

I felt embarrassed. But I also felt good. I took my driver out of the bag and then immediately replaced it. I took out my three iron. My lucky club.

I swung fast and hit the ball hard, with every ounce of strength I had. That, at least, was my intention.

Inevitably, the ball never rose more than a foot off the ground. It bounced along the grass of the tee, rolled along the fairway and came to rest no more than fifty yards away from where I was standing.

'Straight,' said Oliver, with a nod of approval.

'Straight down the middle,' agreed Gerald.

'Safe shot,' said Simon. 'Good choice on this hole.'

I watched as the other three drove off. I thought that perhaps Oliver was lifting his head a little early. And it occurred to me that maybe Gerald needed more follow through. But I didn't say anything. I didn't like to. Later, maybe. When they got to know me better. I didn't care about the topped shot. I really didn't care. There are few things on this earth more pleasing than hitting a good shot. That memory will last. The memory of the bad shots fades quickly. There are so many of them.

'You know the British Open,' I said to Simon, as we strode from the tee side by side.

'It's just called the Open,' he corrected me. 'Only Americans call it the British Open.'

'Right,' I nodded. 'The Open. How do they decide who gets to play?'

'I think anyone can play,' said Simon. 'If they get through the qualifying rounds, of course.'

'You don't have to be a top professional?'

'No. I don't think so. No, I'm pretty sure you don't.'

'An ordinary amateur could enter and win? Just out of nowhere?'

'Yes. Wouldn't that be a dream, eh?' said Simon.

It would, I thought. But I wasn't too happy about the way he said it. It sounded as though it was a dream of his. But it wasn't his dream; it was my dream.

* * *

As we left the 18th green I nearly jumped out of my skin when a lanky man wearing a terrible, tawny-coloured toupee leapt out in front of me. He was dressed entirely in green. Green waterproof jacket. Green waterproof trousers. And, just visible at his neck, a green polo necked sweater. He carried a golf club which he was using as a walking stick. It looked like a five iron. The toupee was the worst and most ill-fitting I'd ever seen. I tried not to stare at it but was not at first entirely convinced that it was supposed to be there at all. Perhaps, I thought, someone had crept up behind him and just plonked it down on his head. I couldn't help wondering how anyone could wear anything quite so absurd and not realise how silly it looked. He would have been less conspicuous in an off-the-shoulder pink chiffon number with diamanté panels and a plunging neckline.

'I've been watching you!' said the face under the toupee fiercely. The owner of the face (and presumably the toupee) waved his club at me. 'You've just played an entire round of golf, haven't you?'

Fearing that I was being accosted by some sort of golfing inspector and was about to be arrested for masquerading as a golfer or bringing the game into disrepute, I nevertheless confessed that I had indeed been attempting to play golf.

'I got a par on the 16th!' I said in my own defence. It suddenly occurred to me that the man might be a talent scout eager to sign me up. Did they have such people in golf, I wondered.

'Have you paid a green fee?' demanded the man with the toupee.

My fear that I must have done something pretty terrible and was about to have my golfing clubs ceremonially shredded subsided when it became clear that my companions were not at all concerned by the club waving interloper. Simon groaned audibly and Oliver muttered something under his breath.

'Oh don't be so bloody stupid Howard,' said Gerald. 'He's a member.'

'Ah,' said Howard, deflating rapidly. 'Is he? Are you sure?'

'Of course we're sure,' said Simon. 'I was one of his proposers. He's got a little badge somewhere. And don't wave that bloody five iron around! Behave yourself or none of us will vote for you next time there is an election.'

Howard, the man with the toupee, hurried away.

* * *

'Who one earth was that?' I asked Simon when we got into the changing rooms.

'That was Howard,' explained Simon. 'Howard is our club chairman. He is probably the most pompous, boring and stupid man I've ever met. He's a local councillor as well as our chairman. He's a joiner.'

'Is he?' said Gerald, surprised. 'I never knew that.'

'Never knew what?'

'That he was a joiner.'

'Of course he's a joiner. He loves joining things and he loves standing for things. If there's an election for anything he'll stand.'

'I thought you meant he was a carpenter,' muttered Gerald, removing his socks.

'He once told me that he was on 34 committees,' said Simon. 'He's the sort of bloke who would have been proud to be president of the Stamp Club at school. When he was first voted onto the club committee he started to behave like a schoolmaster. Now that he's chairman he behaves as though he owns the club. He spends several days a week hiding in the undergrowth to watch out for visiting golfers who play the course without paying a green fee.'

'Does he catch many people?' I asked.

'As far as I know he's never caught anyone,' said Simon.

'I think he did once a couple of seasons ago,' said Gerald, opening his locker. 'But the chap he caught ran off and Howard couldn't catch him.'

'Sometimes we go out in disguise just to give him a thrill,' said Simon. 'We wear false beards and Groucho Marx spectacles and he leaps out of the bushes frothing at the mouth in excitement.'

'I think we ought to stop that,' said Oliver. 'The last time we did it he got so excited I thought he was going to have a heart attack and die.'

'Well if he does die I think we should still vote for him as club chairman,' said Simon. 'A dead chairman would probably be the best sort of chairman.'

Gerald and Oliver thought about this for a moment and then nodded approvingly.

'He'd like that,' agreed Oliver.

'Howard is harmless,' Gerald told me. 'But, as you've seen, he does take himself rather seriously. He never has any opinions of his own but if you make the mistake of asking him his view on anything he will have always had dinner with someone who is very well placed to know the inside story and to have, therefore, formulated the only truly sound view on the subject.'

'He's writing a book,' Simon told me. 'If you promise to print a review you and he will probably get on.'

Gerald and Oliver both turned to look at Simon. Both were clearly astonished. 'What the hell is he writing a book about?' asked Gerald.

'He's writing a book on the history of public car parks. He knows more about public car parks than any man alive or dead. He can tell you how many public car park spaces there are in any British town or city and if you really must know he'll tell you which car parks have the biggest spaces and which have the most competitive prices.'

'I must buy a copy when it comes out,' said Oliver. 'It'll make a wonderful present for my brother-in-law.'

'I thought you hated your brother-in-law?' said Gerald.

'I do,' said Oliver.

'That's his locker,' said Simon, nodding to a locker behind us. I looked across. The locker was decorated with a large picture of a bull.

'He's very proud of that picture,' said Simon. 'He thinks we stuck it there because he's a strong, powerful leader.'

'But you didn't?'

'We put it there because he's full of bullshit,' said Simon.

As I got out of my wet clothes I found a scrap of paper in my jacket pocket. It was an old receipt on which I had scrawled a silly advertisement. As the four of us left the changing room and headed into the bar I tossed it into a rubbish bin.

Chapter Eight

'I Think My Clubs Must Have Warped In The Heat.'

We were playing a variation on the game of golf which I'd never seen before, but at which Simon was surprisingly adept and about which Oliver and Gerald, although considerably less than skilful, were very enthusiastic. The game required a wide-brimmed fedora hat belonging to Oliver and a coffee and alcohol stained pack of playing cards which belonged to the club and were, when not in use, kept behind the bar.

The game was played from four leather armchairs beside the fireplace. Each player had, in turn, to try to flick a playing card into the upturned hat. A card which fell into the centre of the hat counted as one point. A card which rested on the wide brim of the hat scored half a point. A card which fell onto the carpet counted for nothing. If a card resting on the brim fell into the hat the half point was upgraded to one point; if it fell onto the carpet the half point would be deleted.

The game, designed by Simon, involved moving the hat to 18 pre-ordained positions – or 'holes' – around the lounge. Some of the holes were just a few feet away. The furthest 'hole' was fifteen feet away. One hole was perched on top of a bookcase, another was half hidden under a low, glass topped table and a one was situated so dangerously close to the fire that the pack of cards no longer contained a seven of clubs, a three of diamonds or a joker. The fact that some holes were nearer to one player than the others was made irrelevant by the fact that other holes were nearer to other players. Games were usually played as medal play – with the total number of points added up at the end of a round to find the winner. Match play tended to be less exciting because of the large number of holes that were halved, with no one scoring any points at all.

'Brilliant! Good shot!' cried Simon, as Gerald, the first of us to play the 18th hole, flicked a jack of hearts directly into the centre of the hat.

'Your shot Oliver,' said Gerald.

'Make it count,' murmured Simon. 'You need half a point to draw and a full point to win.'

Oliver edged as far forwards as he could in his chair.

'I'm watching you!' Gerald said to him. He turned to me. 'Keep an eye on Oliver's bum for me, will you? His bum has to remain in contact with the chair at all times – before, during and after he takes his shot.'

'I'm sitting on the chair!' exclaimed Oliver. He lifted his bottom, half standing, so that we could see the indentation in the leather cushion of the chair.

'You've raised your bum!' cried Gerald. 'You lose a penalty shot.'

'Don't be daft,' replied Oliver, sitting down again. 'I wasn't taking a shot. I only stood up to show you that I was sitting down.'

'Shut up Gerald,' said Simon. 'Let him get on with it. This is a pressure shot.'

'I know it's a pressure shot,' said Oliver, sounding rather exasperated. 'There's no need to remind me.'

'Sshhh!' whispered Simon, laying a forefinger upright across his lips.

Oliver licked his lips, leant forwards as far as he could legally go, studied the hat carefully and prepared his wrist for the flick. Then, after what seemed like an eternity, he sent the card spinning towards its target.

'Looks good!' said Simon. 'Great shot.'

'It misses,' said Gerald, with certainty, as though he was watching a replay of something he'd seen a dozen times.

Oliver's card, for the record it was the ten of hearts, dipped as it slowed, slightly at first and then more dramatically, and landed on the front rim of the upturned fedora.

'Yes!' Oliver cried, with delight.

But the card wasn't flat when it landed and it didn't stay on the rim. Remarkably, and to Oliver's horror, it flicked upright, bounced, landed on the far rim, where, for a brief moment, it looked as though it would stick, and then slid without further delay onto the carpet.

Oliver groaned. Gerald, beaming like a small boy, clapped his hands together in delight.

'Amazing shot!' said Simon. 'Hard luck old chap.' He clapped Oliver on the back. I added my commiserations to Simon's and congratulated Gerald who was so full of pure delight that I don't think he noticed. It was, I learned later, the first time in his life that he had ever won anything. It was a moment he was clearly determined to savour to the full.

Oliver looked glum. 'That wasn't fair,' he said. 'Just look at that hat!'

Simon and I looked at the hat. Gerald was too busy feeling pleased with himself to look at anything.

'What's wrong with it?' asked Simon.

'It's clearly leaning backwards,' said Oliver. 'If it had been flat on the floor my card would have stayed on the rim. It might even have fallen into the hat.'

'Perhaps,' agreed Simon, who knew Oliver too well, and had played too many games of golf with him, to argue about something as important as this.

Oliver shook his head sadly.

'You get the drinks, old chap,' said Gerald, still grinning and enjoying his moment of glory. 'I'll have a treble and a packet of pork scratchings.' He saw someone he knew on the far side of the room and, overflowing with delight, toddled over to share some of his superfluous delight with someone else.

Oliver, after taking the rest of our orders, limped off towards the bar. Head down, shoulders slumped it wasn't difficult to tell that he had lost.

'Good excuse that,' said Simon, nodding approvingly.

I looked at him.

'The hat not being flat on the floor,' he explained. 'Good excuse.'

I thought for a moment. 'Yes,' I agreed. 'I suppose it was.'

'Original, convincing and doesn't make the mistake of putting the blame on someone who can argue back,' explained Simon.

I murmured something to make it clear that I understood but that making excuses might be thought to make one look a bit like a bad loser.

'Good heavens!' said Simon, clearly shocked. 'Excuses are pretty well the most important part of golf. Now that you've learned a little about the basics of golf you have to understand the finer points. You can't progress within the game, and become a more accomplished player, without learning the art of making good excuses.'

I looked at him, surprised.

'You can't play our sort of golf without getting pretty good at making up appropriate excuses,' insisted Simon. 'Even the complete tyro needs to be conversant with the basics. It's always fair to blame mother nature or the groundsman for a bad shot. A gust of wind took it into the trees. The grass has been watered too much or not enough or is the wrong sort or has been trodden down the wrong way. There were pitch marks or spike marks on the green. The sun was glinting off a sprinkler head. I heard a camera shutter. Someone's mobile phone went off on a nearby tee. Some of the worst golfers I've ever met only ever play wonderful shots. Where the ball ends up – in a bunker, a tree or a stream – is a result of something outside their control. Most golfers will tell you that they are desperately unlucky out on the course. A golfer I knew won the lottery twice and still swore that he was the unluckiest man alive.'

I was shocked by all this. I wasn't particularly shocked by the excuses themselves. I was shocked by the fact that I hadn't even thought to make any of them.

'A good golfer will make damned sure he doesn't ever put himself into a position where he might be stymied and unable to use his best excuses.'

I asked him what he meant by that.

'Well, for example, when I first started playing the game I knew a bloke who played with a set of terribly battered old clubs. The heads were rusty, the shafts were bent and the grips were worn smooth. He wasn't a poor man and he wasn't a mean man but he wouldn't buy himself a new set, even though it was pretty clear to him and to everyone he played with that they were probably costing him shots. One day I asked him straight out why he didn't treat himself to a new set of clubs. And do you know what he said?'

I shook my head.

'He told me that the clubs he had were a wonderful, ever present excuse for all the bad shots he played. 'Whenever I play a bad shot,' he said, 'I just blame my clubs. Everyone I play with can see the clubs are crappy so they accept the excuse. If I buy new clubs and I still play awful golf shots what am I going to blame?" Simon looked at me. 'And he was making a good point. Since then I've known several guys whose game has fallen apart after they've bought new clubs. They feel bereft without their old excuse and so their game deteriorates.' '

I thought for a moment. 'Yes,' I agreed. 'I can understand that.'

'Mind you,' said Simon, 'there is a way out if you find yourself in this situation.'

I waited.

Simon smiled. 'Just blame the new clubs,' he said. 'You simply say that the new clubs aren't right for you. That your game was much better suited to your old clubs and that you miss them terribly and that you wish you hadn't thrown them out.' He paused and wagged a finger. 'In this situation it's vital to have thrown the old clubs out,' he said. 'If you've still got them hanging up in the garage someone will see them and suggest you dust them off and start playing with them again.'

'So you simply turn the new clubs into a new excuse?'

'Absolutely,' agreed Simon. 'The trick is not to over-sell the new clubs too much before you start playing with them. Don't tell everyone that they're wonderful. Explain that your wife has bought them for you and that you feel you really have to dump the old ones and play with the new ones.'

'Prepare the ground for failure,' I suggested.

'Exactly!' said Simon. 'Those are what we call chronic excuses; the sort of excuses you can use for years – whatever the situation might be.' He paused and looked at me. 'You'll need to devise a chronic excuse of your own.'

Gerald, having run out of people to impress with his success, wandered back over and sat down. He was still grinning like a Cheshire cat who has just caught a particularly succulent mouse. 'What are you two talking about?' he asked.

'Excuses,' said Simon. 'I'm just explaining to Tom how important excuses are to the good golfer.'

'Not necessary if you win,' said Gerald with a wink. 'Winners never need excuses.' He slumped back into his chair and clasped his hands in front of his ample stomach. He looked like an advertisement for contentment. I'd never seen him, or indeed anyone else, look so happy.

I asked Simon to give me more examples of good excuses.

'Well, you'll often hear Oliver complaining about his bad back,' said Simon. 'If he hits a ball into the rough he'll drop his club and clutch his back as though he has been crippled by a sudden spasm which came on half way through the shot and which is, of course, the reason why his ball is currently nestling at the bottom of a rabbit hole instead of sitting up, waiting to be hit, on the nice short grass of the fairway.'

'That sounds pretty convincing,' I agreed. I had heard Oliver use this excuse and had offered him sympathy and aspirins. (I had put a packet in my golf bag.) It had never occurred to me that Oliver was simply using backache as an excuse for a bad shot. I had always assumed that he had refused to take the preferred aspirin tablets because he had a bad stomach or didn't like taking pills.

'Another chap I used to play with quite often only ever took out half a dozen clubs. He claimed he couldn't afford more, though he drove a new Mercedes and lived in a smart five-bedroomed house in the posh part of town. He used to say things like: 'Of course, I had to overhit that seven iron because I don't have a six iron' or 'Pity I don't have a wedge. I could have put it much closer with a wedge."

'I like that excuse,' I agreed.

'Dull but effective,' said Simon. 'Chronic excuses tend to be pretty run-of-the-mill,' he went on. 'Flamboyancy doesn't fit well with an excuse that you bring out twice a week. You need something solid and reliable. On the other hand, one-off excuses can be as imaginative as you like. Indeed, there is a strong school of opinion that excuses which are truly bizarre are, in their way, more believable than more mundane excuses. The boy who turns up late for school and complains that the bus was late will get no points for originality and very little sympathy. The boy who reports that he is late because he stopped to help an old lady who had collapsed and that he had to perform cardiac massage for forty minutes while he waited for an ambulance to arrive will, unless the school teacher is mean enough to make enquiries, likely to be congratulated and treated as a hero, rather than given five hundred lines and a good belting with an old plimsoll.'

'They don't do that any more,' I said.

'What don't they do?' asked Simon.

'Teachers aren't allowed to belt children with old plimsolls,' I told him.

'Good God!' cried Simon, genuinely startled. 'How the hell do they keep discipline then?'

'I don't think they do,' I told him.

'And what do they do with all the old plimsolls?'

'Haven't the foggiest. Give me some examples of imaginative golf excuses.'

Simon pulled at an ear lobe (always a sign that he was thinking) and leant back in his chair. 'The best excuses I ever heard came from a chap I knew who was an accountant. He was a member here for years. I played with him one summer. It was a beautiful hot day and he played terribly. I don't think he hit a fairway once. He spent more time playing out of sand than off grass. At the end of the round he tossed his clubs into his car and said: 'I'll have to get rid of those. I left them in the boot during the week. They obviously warped in the heat.'

I laughed. 'And his other excuses?'

'If he played an awful shot, or missed the ball completely – which he was prone to do occasionally – he would whirl round with a terribly excited look on his face and demand: 'Did you hear that? I'm sure it was an Egyptian goose.' He would then study the sky for a minute or two before saying: 'I got completely distracted during my back swing. Did anyone see where my ball went?'

'I must remember that,' I said, impressed.

'Sometimes the simplest excuses are the most effective,' Simon continued. 'If he hit a terrible shot and ended up in thick rough or a huge bunker he would turn round and say: 'This is a very difficult course for me, you know. Just doesn't suit my game."

'Presumably he could use that excuse on any course?'

'Oh absolutely,' agreed Simon. 'And then finally there is the good old 'mud on the ball' excuse. You can only really use this one during the winter months. But it's a good stand-by. When your ball goes flying off to the left you say: 'I thought I'd allowed just enough for the mud on that ball. But I must have over compensated.'

'How on earth do you that?' I asked.

'Do what?'

'Allow for mud on the ball?'

'Haven't the foggiest, old chap. But the beauty of this is that it suggests to your opponent that you know how to hit a ball in such a way as to allow for the effect of the mud sticking to it. I once knew a chap who practised all sorts of variations on this one. One of his favourites was 'I thought there was mud on the underside of the ball. I can never play those shots properly.' Another chap I knew was so fond of this excuse that when the club allowed members to pick their balls up, clean them and replace them he steadfastly refused to do so. 'That's cheating, old boy,' he would frown. What he really meant, of course, was that he didn't want to lose his favourite excuse.'

'Did his partners take advantage of the rule?'

'Hardly ever,' said Simon. 'Not if he was looking. He made them feel that they were cheating even though they weren't.'

'Great stuff. Any more?'

'I once played with an engineer who told me how he adapted something he'd learnt from a friend who was in the navy,' said Simon. 'He'd heard that Morse operators were told not to do any strenuous physical exercise involving their arms before transmitting Morse because it was known that too much exercise will temporarily interfere with the ability of the muscles to perform accurate tasks.'

'Go on,' I said.

'Well this chap said that he'd just done some supermarket shopping for his mother, who was ill in bed, and that he'd carried so many heavy bags that his muscles were ruined for golf. He said his arms had been stretched so far that he could tie his shoelaces without bending down.'

'Brilliant!' I agreed.

'You will have noticed that in addition to creating the excuse he also managed to get our sympathy by telling us about his sick mother and on top of that showed us what a good chap he is because he'd done her shopping.'

I agreed that this was a terrific piece of creative excuse making. 'Was his mother sick?' I asked. 'Had he really done her shopping?'

'He'd never been in a supermarket in his life,' said Simon. 'And I found out later that his mother was a permanent resident in a hotel in Benidorm.'

'Is he still a member?' I asked.

'Sadly, no,' said Simon. 'Unless they've built a course at Wormwood Scrubs he doesn't play much these days.'

'He's in prison?'

'He was sent down for what he claimed was 'creative accounting' but which the judge insisted was 'fraud',' said Simon. 'Unfortunately for him the jury thought the judge's argument was more convincing.'

Just then Oliver came back with the drinks. 'I've been talking to people about what happened,' he told us. 'The general feeling is that if the hat isn't in exactly the same position when the last player takes his turn as it was when the first player has his go then everyone should retake their shot.'

Gerald, hearing this, sat up. 'That's nonsense!' he cried. 'If the wind gets up after one player has driven off, the others don't insist that he has another shot!'

'It's not the same thing at all,' insisted Oliver. 'If someone moved the green after one player had driven it wouldn't be fair would it?'

'How could anyone move a green?' demanded Gerald, not unreasonably.

'Someone might say that everyone had to drive to a different green,' said Oliver.

'This is silly,' said Gerald. 'You just can't accept the fact that you lost.'

'It's not a question of winning or losing,' insisted Oliver. 'It's a question of doing things the right way. Without rules and laws we would all be living in a state of anarchy.'

'And what is wrong with anarchy?' demanded Gerald. 'I sometimes think we all need a little more anarchy.'

Simon stood up, took two small steps over to where I was sitting and bent down. 'This could go on for some time,' he whispered. 'Do you fancy a game of darts?'

I loathe darts. I have no fancy for it, no talent for it and I have always regarded it as a dull game, best kept for overweight alcoholics. 'Fine,' I murmured. 'Good idea.'

We picked up the drinks which Oliver had bought us, promised to be back shortly, and wandered over towards the dartboard.

Chapter Nine

'Your Tee Is In The Oven.'

I was sitting in the clubhouse one Sunday morning, wondering whether to stay where I was, sitting by the window, watching other golfers battle against yet another unexpected summer gale, or to venture forth and do battle with the winds myself. The only other member present was an elderly fellow called Onions who had never been known to say anything other than to order more gin and never known to do anything else other than sleep. He slept for upwards of ten hours a day. Onions was, I suppose, a harmless enough fellow though he did have a tendency to snore rather loudly. The snoring did, however, have the advantage of being fairly rhythmical and predictable and after fifteen or twenty minutes I found that my mind would disregard the noise in the same sort of way that one's mind gets accustomed to, and takes no real notice of, the hum of a central heating system or a ship's engine.

I was alone because my usual playing companions had all had to cry off for the same reason – it was Father's Day.

'It's Father's Day on Sunday,' Simon had moaned. 'So I can't play.'

'Why ever not?' I asked him.

'The kids insist on making a fuss of me and giving me a good time,' he complained, miserably. 'I played last year on Father's Day and no one spoke to me for a week afterwards.'

This all seemed rather odd to me. After all, since Simon wanted nothing more than to spend his Sunday at the golf club you would have thought that it would have made sense for his family to allow him to do just that. The whole idea of Father's Day is, after all, to indulge the father and make him happy.

But I quickly discovered that Simon was by no means the only father who was expected to stay at home and give up his day's pleasure so that his family could keep him at home and make him 'happy'.

'Oh no, dammit,' said Oliver, when he learnt that it was Father's Day.

'Not you as well!' I said in some surprise.

'Afraid so,' admitted Oliver. 'I sneaked out after breakfast twelve years ago and afterwards they made me feel so guilty that I swore I'd never do it again. It wasn't worth it. My wife told me that the kids had spent a month planning on ways to give me a good day.'

'How old are your children?' I asked Oliver. I had never met his wife or his children and knew very little about his home life.

Oliver had to think for a moment. 'My boy, that's Sebastian, is 22,' he replied at last. 'Or he may be 23.' He paused and thought again. 'No, 22,' he said. 'And my daughter is two years older.'

I was surprised by this. I had expected him to tell me that his children were seven or eight years old.

'It's the lady wife who makes all the fuss,' said Oliver. 'I don't think the kids really care. It's probably as much of a chore for them as it is for me. But the wife regards Father's Day as second only to Christmas on the family calendar.'

'Well it's nice that they all care,' I told him.

'I suppose so,' he admitted. 'But I wish they cared enough to let me play golf. My idea of a nice, restful day is to play a gentle round of golf with my pals, have a nice pie and chips with a couple of beers, then another round of golf followed up with a whisky or two.'

Gerald's son was also old enough to have children of his own. But Gerald, long divorced, was expected to turn up for the day's festivities and to play endless games of blind man's buff and garden cricket.

* * *

So, Simon, Gerald and Oliver were all at home being presented with new pipes, carpet slippers and multi-function penknives while

I, childless and therefore exempt from the celebrations, was sitting in a virtually deserted lounge bar at the golf club. Onions had got himself into a nice, steady rhythm and all seemed well with the world.

I had survived one scary moment earlier in the day.

Howard, the club chairman had cornered me and treated me to a fifteen minute monologue on the beauties and practicalities of municipal car parks in North East England. He had, I think, been about to invite me to walk round the course looking for visitors who hadn't paid their green fees when, much to my relief, he had been spirited away by two members of the Works Committee who had insisted on taking him away for an in-depth discussion on the state of the roof of the tractor shed.

I had once expressed mild and polite interest in car parks and Howard had never forgotten this. The result of my indiscretion was that if Howard ever entered the lounge and spotted me sitting alone he would beetle over for an impromptu discussion of his favourite subject.

But the two works committee members had saved me from Howard and I was now daydreaming while digesting my light lunch and pretending to plough my way through the endless supplements of one of the Sunday newspapers (I doubt if anyone actually reads these things but scattering a Sunday newspaper around does provide excellent camouflage if one is intent on preserving a little privacy in a public place) when my relatively peaceful reverie was disturbed by a voice I vaguely recognised.

'Here's the plumber; he's not doing anything! He's new but he'll do nicely.'

I had been playing long enough to discard the wrist bandolier which the professional had sold me and I now kept a couple of golf tees in the left hand pocket of every pair of trousers I owned. The little mechanical clicker I had bought, so that I could keep score without having to carry a score card and a stub of pencil, was now lying forgotten in my desk drawer at work. And instead of using the ball washer I now cleaned my balls by spitting on them and polishing them on my trousers. But despite all this I was, I knew, still fairly new at golf.

I opened my eyes, blinked, and looked around. Standing directly in front of me was the woman in the tweed skirt whom I had met on my very first visit to the club. It was, I felt confident, the same tweed skirt that she'd been wearing then. This time she was wearing something above the waist: a cream blouse, decorated with pearl buttons down the front. On her left stood the blonde whom I had also met in the showers. The blonde with the muscles. On her right stood a middle-aged man wearing a bright yellow sweater and a pair of lime green trousers.

'Finishing lunch?'

The remains of a bowl of potato wedges and a tomato salad were on the table in front of me. I confirmed the accuracy of this observation.

'Good food?'

'Splendid.'

I'd started eating lunch at the golf club quite regularly. The food was better than that in most of the local pubs and, during the week at least, the clubhouse was usually fairly quiet at lunchtime. Because of the nature of my job, my working hours were flexible. If the weather was good I could play a round, or half a round, after lunch and then go back to the office and work in the evening.

'We were never properly introduced.' said the woman in the tweed skirt. 'I'm Flo. Short for Florence. This is my husband Ebeneezer. We call him Eb for short.' Looking at Flo I realised that she wasn't quite as old as I had previously thought. She was, I now suspected, somewhere in her mid forties. I hadn't liked to look too hard when she was in the shower because she'd been half naked.

'He's a plumber?' said Eb.

I toyed with the idea of trying to demolish this now well-established myth but decided that in view of the circumstances in which I had met Flo and the blonde with muscles it would be more sensible to say nothing. Fully-clothed and shod the blonde looked even more formidable than she had when standing naked in the shower.

'He sorted out the drain in the shower room,' said Flo.

'Have you told him about our dripping tap?'

'Later,' said Flo firmly. 'We need a fourth,' she said to me.

'A fourth?'

'For a game of foursomes.'

'Oh.'

'My usual partner broke his toe,' said the blonde. She held out a hand. 'We weren't ever introduced either. I'm Daphne.' She crushed my hand with a grip that would have turned Oddjob's fingers to dust. She was wearing a bright blue sweater decorated with a small pink zebra embroidered above her left breast and a pair of black Lycra cycling shorts which clung to her well-muscled thighs like clingfilm. She wore a blue cap with a long curved peak and her blonde hair was tied into a ponytail and was poking through the gap in the back of the cap.

'Tom,' I said. 'I'm sorry.'

'Oh I don't mind,' said Daphne. 'Lots of people have bloody silly names. Doesn't bother me.'

'No, no,' I said. 'About your partner I mean.'

'Oh don't be,' she said. 'Own stupid fault. In the gym and dropped a pile of weights on his toes. Can't walk.'

'I haven't been playing long,' I said. 'I'm not terribly good.'

'Don't worry about that!' laughed Daphne. 'We'll hold your hand.'

Despite this reassurance I was still a little alarmed. This was the first time I had ever played a game of foursomes although I was, of course, aware of the existence of this rather curious variation on the game of golf.

I had been watching four players meander up the 18th fairway when it occurred to me that there was something odd about the way they were playing. Eventually, it had occurred to me that although there were four players they were playing with just two balls. I had asked Gerald what was going on and he had explained that two players on each side took it in turn to play the same ball.

'Oh, that's a good idea,' I said. 'I suppose they're running a bit low.' I naturally assumed that since they were now travelling up the 18th fairway they'd had a rather tempestuous round of golf. The alternative explanation, that they were unable to afford more than one golf ball between two, I had suppressed since golfers, like everyone else, are sometimes sensitive to suggestions that they might not be able to afford something and I did not want to upset anyone. 'Do you think I should totter out and offer them a few more balls?' I had asked but Gerald had not thought this was a good idea.

'I like foursomes,' said Flo, the woman in the tweed skirt. 'You never have to take responsibility for your own bad shots, and you can always blame someone else when you find yourself with a tricky lie.'

Her husband, Eb, lowered his head a little. I got the impression that he wasn't quite so keen on the foursome format.

'Handicap?' Daphne asked me.

'I, er, haven't got one yet,' I muttered, feeling rather embarrassed by this.

'Hundred?' Flo asked Daphne.

'Fine by us,' said Daphne.

I looked at her, waiting for a translation.

'We're playing for a hundred quid,' Daphne told me. 'Fifty each. OK?'

'Er, OK,' I said. I had never played golf for real money before.

Daphne turned to the woman in the tweed skirt, who was clearly the spokeswoman for herself and her husband. 'We'll need some odds in our favour,' she said firmly.

'We'll give you two throws and a shout,' said Flo.

'Not enough,' said Daphne, shaking her head so furiously that her ponytail swung from side to side.

'What do you want?'

'Three throws, three shouts and two negative mulligans,' said Daphne.

'We'll give you two throws, two shouts and two negative mulligans,' replied Flo after some thought.

'Done,' said Daphne instantly.

'Isn't he any good?' asked Eb, as the negotiations ended.

'Apparently not,' said Flo.

'I hope he's not a ringer,' said Eb.

'Doesn't look like one,' said Flo.

'That's the whole point,' muttered Eb. 'They never do.'

I hadn't understood any of the negotiating that had gone on.

'What was all that about?' I asked Daphne as Eb and Flo scuttled off to their respective changing rooms to prepare themselves for the match. Daphne, it was clear, was already changed.

'Just an informal way of handicapping a match,' she told me, and proceeded to explain how it worked.

There are, she told me, a variety of ways of giving opponents who are less skilful a chance to play a match on a more equal footing.

First, a player may give an opponent a chance either to pick up his own ball and throw it nearer to the hole or an opportunity to pick up his opponent's ball and throw it further away from the hole – and deeper into trouble. That is a 'throw'.

Second, a player can have the right to shout out loud just as a player is taking his or her shot. That is a 'shout'.

'This can be pretty devastating,' Daphne explained. 'You don't just get a chance to wreck a player's shot with this. If you use this properly it can destroy a whole round. Every time you stand near to your opponent he'll be waiting for the shout to come.'

'Do you have to shout anything in particular?' I asked.

'No. Anything you like.'

'Does it have to be on the tee? Or the green?'

'No. Anywhere you like.'

Third, there is a negative mulligan. Taking a mulligan, I had already learned from Simon, means simply re-taking a shot that you aren't pleased with. A negative mulligan is exactly the opposite – it means making your opponent retake a shot when he's just played a shot that he's really pleased with.

Fourth, a player who needs extra help can opt for either a simple or a radical clubectomy. A simple clubectomy gives the inferior player the chance to choose and remove a club from the better player's bag. A radical clubectomy gives the player the chance to remove several clubs – usually three, five or seven – from the better player's bag. Given the opportunity of a radical clubectomy a wise player will remove the putter and all the wedges – leaving the better player to get round the course with only woods and long irons.

Fifth, an inferior player may force a better player to use a single club (usually selected by the inferior player) from green to tee on a specified hole. As a variation on this, the inferior player may simply be allowed to tell the better player which club he must use for a particular shot.

Naturally, all this needs to be negotiated before the match starts. Daphne had negotiated for us two of No 1, two No 2s and two No 3s and what sounded like a selection from a Chinese menu meant that we had two throws, two shouts and two negative mulligans.

Although I suspected that Daphne knew how to play golf I didn't think it sounded anywhere near enough.

* * *

Daphne and I met our opposition on the first tee. Eb was now wearing a pair of bright yellow trousers and a lime green sweater. It didn't seem much of an improvement on his previous choice of outfit. Flo had changed out of the tweed skirt and pearl-buttoned blouse and was now wearing a pair of plaid trousers, a thick polo necked sweater in dark blue, a bright red anorak and a blue woolly hat which was decorated with a green bobble. The bobble was, for some reason, on a long piece of wool so that every time Flo moved her head the bobble bounced around like a ball on a piece of elastic.

'I took up golf because I had become a golf widow,' Flo told me. 'I'm not going to say anything about that,' she said, putting an enormous amount of emphasis on the final word. There was a long pause and it was obvious that she was acting as her own straight woman and that the punchline was still to come. 'Though I could say a lot,' she added, looking at me archly. She stared at me for several seconds; so long that I felt distinctly uncomfortable. I couldn't look away. I felt mesmerised, like a rabbit transfixed by a stoat or whatever wild creature it is that transfixes rabbits with its glare. 'He'd been playing for years when I started but I'm a better player than he is now.'

'Oh I wouldn't say that, dear,' protested Eb. 'I could have been a contender,' he added so quietly that Flo, who was rummaging in her golf bag, couldn't hear him. 'I could have been a contender,' Eb whispered to me. 'At the top level.' I nodded approvingly. I knew the feeling.

Flo found a ball and a tee and handed them to her husband,

who put the former on the latter and pulled an elderly-looking iron out of his bag.

'It was no life at all,' complained Flo. 'He used to go out on a Saturday morning at dawn and he wouldn't come home until midnight. It was the same on Sundays.'

Eb didn't waste time on practice swings. He stood up to the ball, took one gentle swing and sent the ball flying 150 yards down the centre of the fairway. He bent down, picked up the tee, put it back into his golf bag and turned. 'We always had lunch with your mother on Sundays,' he pointed out.

'That was alternate Sundays and you used to play a round in the morning and another in the afternoon. We got you for an hour in between,' said Flo firmly.

'Shall I start us off or will you?' Daphne asked me.

'Oh you, please,' I said, delighted to delay my entrance into the match for as long as possible.

Daphne unwrapped a brand new ball and put it onto a long wooden tee. She pulled out a driver, tossed the red plastic cover which she had taken from the club's head onto the grass, took two or three practice swishes at a long piece of grass which had escaped the groundsman's mower, and then proceeded to send our ball flying well over two hundred yards down the left of the fairway. It came to rest in thin rough but didn't seem to be lying too badly.

'I am very fond of your mother,' said Eb.

'Then he started playing on weekdays too,' said Flo. 'I got so fed up one day that I left a message on his mobile phone telling him that his tea was in the oven.'

Eb looked embarrassed but said nothing. Daphne had now put the cover back on her driver and had put her driver back into her bag. She set off down the fairway at quite a pace. She swayed along from side to side as she walked; strolling along like a woman who is in a hurry but wearing Wellington boots that are several sizes too big for her.

'It was very clever of me,' said Flo. 'When he looked in the oven what do you think he found?'

I hesitated. 'His tea?' I suggested.

'A tee!' said Flo. She laughed rather hysterically. 'It was a trick.

I put a blue plastic golf tee in the oven because I hadn't made him any tea.' She looked at me. 'What do you think of that? Clever, eh?'

'Very clever,' I agreed, running after my partner.

It was Flo's turn to play next. She sent their ball bouncing down the right side of the fairway and although it never went more than six feet high it travelled well over a hundred yards in the direction of the green. The right direction.

I made a mess of my attempt to extricate our ball from the thin rough. Instead of reaching the green, as I had hoped, I sent the ball a yard deeper into trouble where it nestled down in thicker grass and looked pretty unplayable.

'Sorry,' I muttered to Daphne.

'Don't worry about it,' she said. She took an iron from her bag and with an astonishing display of power managed to extricate the ball, and send it and a huge divot well down the fairway.

'When do we use our throws and things?' I asked her, as we walked along together. Eb and Flo were now on the other side of the fairway and well out of earshot.

'Oh, we'll probably wait a while,' said Daphne. 'We'll use them when we can get the best out of them.' I didn't ask anything else. I was using up all my breath keeping up with her. I had never known a woman walk so quickly.

'After that I decided to follow the old motto 'If you can't beat 'em, join 'em',' said Flo, when we all finally reached the green. I had totally lost track of how many we or they had taken. I couldn't even remember whose shot it was next. 'When I started to play Eb wanted to teach me,' continued Flo. 'He said it would save money but I suspect he was worried about me spending time with another man.' She laughed and looked at Eb who said nothing. It was difficult to believe that Eb would have been jealous if she'd gone away for the weekend with the local rugby team. Her laugh was terrifying. She sounded like a pantomime villain. 'It was disastrous,' she continued. She shuddered as though the memory of the experience still upset her. 'I knew instinctively that he was doing everything wrong. And I was absolutely right, of course. Wasn't I, Eb?'

Eb was by now busy cleaning their ball. He grunted something incomprehensible.

'We rowed all the time,' she continued. 'So I took lessons from a professional. Not Walter, of course. A lady professional. Frightfully good and nowhere near as expensive as Walter. A beautiful girl who offers lessons part time. The men don't like lady professionals, of course, so she has to moonlight as an estate agent to make ends meet. Now I play better than Eb. Don't I dear?' She paused and winked to let me know that a joke was coming. 'Not that that would be difficult!' she laughed.

Daphne and I lost that hole.

'Don't worry about it,' muttered Daphne, as we strode together towards the next tee. 'And try to ignore Flo. She'll drive you potty if you let her talk at you all the time.'

'How do I stop her talking?' I asked in desperation.

'Just ignore her,' said Daphne. 'We all do. She soon gets tired and shuts up.'

* * *

We lost the next hole, drew the one after that and lost the fourth and fifth so that by the time we stood on the sixth tee we were in the, it seemed to me, uncomfortable position of being four down. Daphne, however, didn't seem to be in the slightest bit worried. 'We haven't used any of our handicap assets yet,' she whispered, as we stood at the back of the tee. I looked at her, puzzled, and frowned. 'Handicap assets,' she repeated. 'Our throws, shouts and negative mulligans.' Up ahead Flo and Eb were deciding which club Eb should use to drive off with. Flo kept turning round to look at us.

'When do we use them?' I asked.

'Soon,' whispered Daphne. She spoke so low that I couldn't hear her properly. I told her this. She reached out a large hand and pulled my ear close to her mouth. 'Soon,' she whispered. 'But not yet. Try to look shifty and move forward a yard or so.' She let go of my head. I moved forward. I don't think I had to work at looking shifty. I didn't have the faintest idea what was going on.

'Go on, quickly,' said Flo suddenly, looking over her shoulder at me. Eb, who had already put their ball on a tee, took a quick backswing, much faster than usual, and jabbed at the ball which squirted off the tee to the left. It went over a fence and into a field.

'What a pity,' said Daphne. 'Hard luck Eb. Out of bounds. You're playing three off the tee.'

She strode forwards, teed up and drove straight down the middle.

'What was all that about?' I asked her as we walked down the fairway. Eb and Flo were searching for their ball on the other side of the fairway. Their second shot had squirted right.

'They were expecting us to use one of our 'shouts' there,' said Daphne. 'Eb got so flustered at trying to make his drive before you could shout out behind him that he put it out of bounds.'

'Ah,' I said. 'So we got a sort of bonus.'

'Exactly,' agreed Daphne. 'That's the whole beauty of free shouts. The longer you go before using them the more the other chaps worry about them. Sometimes one free shout will be enough to devastate the other side – especially if you don't use it until the 18th hole. All the way round they'll be waiting for you to use it – expecting a shout just as they're driving or putting or trying to get out of a bunker. And by the time they get to the 18th they'll be jumping and yipping all over the place.'

She was right.

We didn't see much of our opponents until we reached the putting surface but on the green they were constantly on edge, waiting for one of us to shout and put them off their stroke. We won the hole easily. And we won the next one too, without having to use up any of our throws, shouts or negative mulligans.

* * *

By the time we reached the turn we were just two down.

'I almost feel bad about this,' I said to Daphne as we stood on the tee for the start of the return nine. 'Flo is beginning to look very edgy. Every time I move she jumps a foot. Don't you think we should put them out of their misery and use up our shouts?'

'With £100 at stake? Not bloody likely.'

We lost the tenth to go back to three down and I suddenly felt less generous. I was beginning to wonder whether Daphne might have left it too late.

On the next hole we had to use up two of our assets to win the hole. After Eb had driven beautifully, and I had hooked my tee shot into a pond, it looked as though we were starting the hole in a bad position. Our second shot was on the fairway but only about 150 yards away from the tee.

'We really need to win this hole,' said Daphne. 'If we lose this one we'll be four down with seven to go. Not nice.'

I nodded.

'Take that one again please Eb,' called Daphne, as our opponents headed off down the fairway. Eb and Flo both turned.

'We're using one of our negative mulligans,' explained Daphne.

'Oh Daphne!' said Eb. 'That was my best drive of the match.'

'I know it was Eb,' said Daphne. 'That's why we're making you take it again.'

Eb's second drive was dismal by comparison. He was so angry that he tried to hit the ball still further and ended up hooking it into the same pond that had swallowed my first drive. By the time we reached the green we had taken the same number of shots. It was our turn to putt first. Our ball was a good 40 feet from the hole and Daphne managed to send her putt to within a yard. Flo putted their ball to within inches. When I missed the short putt Daphne immediately bent down, picked up the ball Eb was about to tap in and threw it as hard as she could. It ended up in trees forty yards away from the green. We had used up a shout and a throw on the same hole but we were now just two down.

* * *

We won the next hole by throwing their ball back into a bunker just after Eb and Flo had taken two to get out of it. With six holes to go we were left us with one throw, one shout and a single negative mulligan.

'It's going to be close,' said Daphne. 'Eb is playing as well as I've ever seen him play. I think he must have given up his lessons again.' She explained that every now and then Eb would take a course of lessons from the professional and that when he did he would become so confused at having to remember where to put his knees and elbows that he wouldn't be able to hit the ball properly at all. His swing would look good and his joints and limbs would be perfectly positioned but the ball would either stay where it was or fly off into the nearest patch of jungle.

We lost the thirteenth to go two down again. We had never once been ahead in the match and the only time we'd been all square had been on the first hole.

But the fourteenth was ours.

Eb and Flo were on the green in two. We were on the green in three. Eb's putt was a long, curling, beautifully weighted shot which hung on the edge of the cup but wouldn't drop. My first putt was my best shot of the match. From twelve feet I left the ball less than a foot from the hole. If Daphne holed it, which I was sure she would, we would be down in five. But Flo had a putt of less than an inch for a four.

'Sorry about this, Eb,' said Daphne, bending down and picking up his ball. 'But I'm afraid that was just too good a shot.' She threw the ball into a deep bunker at the front of the green. 'If you can get down in two from there you'll halve the hole,' she told them.

They took three to finish the hole. We won by one.

So, at the start of the 15th we were one down. We had one negative mulligan and one shout left. I didn't think it would be enough. Daphne was playing well but my inexperience was beginning to show. Occasionally I would hit a decent shot but most of the time I failed to capitalise on Daphne's good shots and ended up leaving her to play a marvellous recovery shot to get us out of trouble.

We lost the sixteenth by at least four shots and there was no use in wasting our one remaining negative mulligan on the hole.

But the seventeenth was different. Eb's second shot was beautiful. A long three iron which faded into the green. As soon as the ball had left his club he turned to where Daphne and I were standing and sighed. 'Again?' he said, sadly.

'Afraid so,' said Daphne. 'It was just too good, Eb.'

'I'll try and put it closer this time,' he said. But he didn't. He put too much fade on the ball and ended up in a bunker. We won the hole by one shot and stood on the eighteenth tee one down and with just one shout left.

'You've left it too late,' said Flo. 'We know you're going to shout now. That makes it easier.' She put a ball on a tee and drove it straight down the middle. Neither Daphne nor I had as much as murmured.

Daphne drove well, fifty yards further than Flo and just as straight. Eb's shot landed just short of the green. My shot almost rolled into a bunker but didn't. We needed to win the hole to draw the match. Flo chipped to about eight feet. Daphne chipped and ran and left the ball two foot closer to the hole.

'If we get this one in you've lost because you can't win,' said Eb, stooping over his putt.

The ball didn't go in. It didn't go anywhere near the hole. It ended up off the far edge of the green. And I thought I was going to have a heart attack. Just as Eb's putter moved backwards Daphne let out the most horrifying scream I'd ever heard. It was so loud and so fierce that people on the practice green called over to see if everything was well. I was told later that someone in the bar rang the police and told them she'd heard someone being stabbed to death. (Naturally, the police didn't bother to turn up so no explanation was required.)

'It'll take them at least two to get down from there,' whispered Daphne. 'So you don't need to get the ball in. Just try to put it close to the hole.'

Relieved of the pressure to hole the ball I holed it. We won the hole by two shots and drew the match. Daphne grabbed me and kissed me on the cheek and I nearly had a heart attack again.

She was, I discovered, every bit as strong as she looked.

* * *

'Throw for the win?' suggested Daphne as we stood beside the 18th green shaking hands.

I assumed that she was suggesting that we toss a coin to decide the result.

Eb and Flo conferred for a moment.

'OK,' said Flo. 'Eb will throw for us.'

'I'll throw for us,' said Daphne. She looked at me. 'That all right with you?'

I said it was fine and asked her if she wanted a coin. I told her that I had a lucky sixpence she could borrow if she liked. She looked at me and shook her head. 'No,' she said. 'You don't understand. Eb and I are going to throw clubs to decide the winner.'

I must have looked as puzzled as I felt.

'Whoever throws a club the furthest is the winner,' she said.

'Which club do you throw?' I asked.

'Anything we like,' replied Daphne. 'I always throw a wedge. Heavier club head and shorter shaft. Goes further. I've spent hours testing this out.'

I told her I had every confidence in her.

My confidence was not misplaced. We walked to the practice ground for this final phase of the competition. Daphne managed to throw her wedge 28 feet further than Eb could throw his putter. We won £50 each.

'This doesn't mean I've lost my amateur status, does it?' I asked Daphne, as she handed me my half of our winnings.

Daphne thought about this for a moment. 'Safest thing is probably not to tell anyone,' she said.

It had not been an afternoon packed with laughs but I had learned a lot.

Chapter Ten

'I'll Put Myself Down For A Five On That Last Hole.'

I had been playing golf for some months before I discovered that not everyone always plays the game in the way that might have won the approval of the dear old Marquess of Queensberry, had he been a golfer which, as far as I know, he wasn't though he did, of course, once threaten to do unspeakable things to Oscar Wilde with a wedge.

I played one Friday morning with a bloke called Kevin. He was, it seemed, one of those people who are unembarrassable. On the first short hole I took eleven. He claimed a three, though I saw him take at least seven or eight swishes at his ball when it landed in thick couch grass at the back of the green.

'I was just swishing in the grass to clean the sand off my wedge,' he told me afterwards when I showed surprise at his score.

'That's as corny as the apocryphal story of the chap who came out of the trees and insisted that five of the six shots he seemed to have played were, in fact, simply attempts to scare away a snake,' said Gerald. 'I didn't think anyone would dare try anything like that these days.'

'I once played a four-ball with three salesmen from Barnsley,' said Oliver. 'They spent half an hour on a tough par five. Balls were raining into the lake like hail and clubs were being hurled through the air so frequently that I half thought of dodging back to borrow a motorcycle helmet from the bar steward. They were hacking and cursing and cursing and hacking and most of the time, although I could hear them, they were so well hidden in the undergrowth that I couldn't see them at all. At the end of the hole one guy was putting for a four, one was putting for a three and the other, who had five putted to within a yard was standing over his ball muttering that if he missed the shot he would be down for a bogey.' He looked at me, pursed lips and nodded knowingly. 'I know what you mean,' he said. 'It's painful to see people cheating so badly.'

'He didn't even seem embarrassed!' I told Simon, Gerald and Oliver. 'When I spotted him moving his marker a yard nearer to the hole he didn't even blush.' 'He claimed a five on the third,' I said. 'But I clearly saw him knock two balls into deep rough and I'm damned certain he didn't find either of them. He had two drives off the tee – he claimed the first one was just a practice shot. And I counted four putts though he did say at the time that one of those didn't count because he'd been stung by a wasp and his arm had jerked involuntarily.'

'So you think he probably took more than five?'

'I'm sure he did. At least eleven.'

Oliver shook his head sadly. 'Sloppy,' he said.

'Sloppy?' I said.

'It's difficult to have respect for a chap who cheats as badly as that,' said Oliver. 'There's cheating and then there's cheating. That's *cheating*.'

'It's very tiring, playing with chaps like that,' said Gerald. 'You can't leave them alone for a second. If they're in a bunker you have to be in there with them – counting out loud.'

'Was there money involved?' asked Oliver.

'We were playing for a pound a hole.'

'Ah, well, to be fair, when money is involved everyone tends to adjust the odds in their favour a bit,' said Oliver. 'Unless you happen to be a great deal better than your opponent, or able to persuade him to give you more strokes or holes than he should, your success will, if you don't want to cheat, depend upon improving your own game.'

'And, naturally, that's out of the question,' interrupted Gerald, shaking his head. 'Trying to improve your game artificially, through practice, is cheating. It also involves a lot of hard work and effort and is immeasurably tedious.'

Confused by all this, and rather having lost sight of the high moral ground from which I had, I thought, begun my attack on cheating, I stared, first at one and then at the other.

'It's very difficult to decide where cheating begins and ends,' said Gerald. 'But I do think that practice should be regarded as cheating.'

'How can practice be cheating?' I asked, astonished.

'If you regard cheating as doing something to give you an unfair advantage over your opponent then practising certainly falls into the category of cheating,' said Gerald. 'If two golfers play a match together but golfer A has spent several hours an evening practising he's given himself an advantage over golfer B hasn't he?'

I agreed that he had. 'But golfer B could practise if he wanted to,' I pointed out.

'He may not be able to practise,' said Gerald. 'Maybe he has family commitments. Or a demanding job which doesn't allow him the time to practise. Maybe he has a dodgy back and daren't hit too many golf balls.'

'Moreover,' continued Gerald, 'when you think about it carefully, practising is admitting that you aren't any good. The more you practise the more you confirm your suspicion that you aren't any good.' He said that whenever professional golfers suddenly lose their skills it is always because they have been taking too many lessons, practising too much and trying too hard. He told me that a friend of his had won three club tournaments in a single season but that the following summer his handicap had ballooned from 6 to 16. 'I know what happened,' said Gerald. 'He believed he could become a scratch golfer and spent the whole winter practising hard. And he overdid it. He became obsessed with improving his golf swing.' Gerald said he went round to the fellow's house one rainy day and found him practising his swing in the living room. 'He had a camcorder set up on a tripod,' said Gerald. 'And he was practising with a new set of clubs he'd just bought. There wasn't much room for a grown man to take a full-blooded golf swing and after the chap had smashed two vases and a clock I asked him if he wasn't worried about doing any damage. 'Oh no,' the fellow replied. 'There isn't much danger of that. These clubs are made of titanium and carbon fibre and stuff like that. They're pretty much indestructible." Gerald said he knew then that the fellow was doomed.

I wasn't sure that Gerald's argument was entirely logical but I couldn't think of a way to counter it.

Gerald hadn't finished.

'Besides, you could use your argument about practice being available to everyone to condone all sorts of things,' continued Gerald. 'If golfer A kicks his ball out of a footprint in a bunker would you say that was cheating?'

'Of course it is.'

'But you could kick your ball out of a footprint if you wanted to.'

'But I wouldn't want to,' I said. 'That would be cheating.'

'You've just argued that practising isn't cheating because both players can do it if they want to,' said Gerald. 'You can't have it both ways.'

I felt sure that this argument didn't stand up but I couldn't put my finger on why. '

'There is, of course, a way of cheating without cheating,' said Oliver. 'It involves preventing the person you're playing against from playing to their ability – in other words, helping them play worse than they might otherwise have done.'

'That isn't cheating?'

'Good heavens no!' said Gerald, clearly startled that I should even ask the question. 'You simply win by encouraging your opponent to take *more* strokes rather than winning by managing to take *fewer* strokes yourself.'

'It's a sport in itself,' said Oliver. 'Very nearly an art form actually.'

'You get to a point as a golfer when you realise that the only way forward is to give yourself a bit of an edge; adjust the odds in your favour a tad,' said Gerald.

'Listen,' said Oliver, 'After three months I decided that I was going to have to concentrate on the part of the game I'm best at.'

'What's that?' I asked.

'Cheating,' said Gerald.

'No, not at all!' said Oliver indignantly. 'Cheating involves breaking the rules. I won't have anything to do with that. There are better ways to improve one's chances of winning than through cheating. Legal, subtle ways of adjusting the odds in one's favour without putting one at risk of getting caught and being humiliated.'

'We should write a book and call it 'How to cheat at golf without actually cheating – and definitely without getting caught',' said Simon. 'We'd make a fortune.'

'You have to be subtle,' said Gerald. He turned to Oliver. 'That's the keyword, wouldn't you agree?'

'Absolutely,' nodded Oliver. 'Subtle. Your opponent should never know what's happening. At the end of the round he should hand over his money convinced that you're a good egg and have beaten him fair and square. He may feel that he's played below his best but he'll believe, in his heart, that on the day the best man won.'

'So what on earth are you talking about?' I demanded.

'The first rule is that you must be friendly,' said Gerald. 'Never be obvious. Never try sledging, for example.'

Oliver shook his head and made a face as though he'd sucked a lemon thinking it was an orange. 'Sledging is terribly crude. Very Australian.'

'Never try to needle your opponent,' said Gerald. 'Not obviously at least.'

'For example, if the chap you're playing with hits the ball no more than a hundred yards you don't laugh at him,' said Oliver. 'Instead you find some way to congratulate him. Be friendly. Tell him that for his age he's doing brilliantly well.'

'Be helpful,' said Gerald. 'If he's got a problem make sure that you draw attention to it. In a spirit of helpfulness of course. If he's slicing the ball every time he drives then when you are standing on the tee you should draw his attention to all the problems on the right of the fairway. If he's hooking the ball, draw his attention to all the problems on the left.'

'Remind him of the shots he's missed that would have got him a birdie or won him a hole,' said Simon. 'Just asking a fellow if he's got over the yips can be worth ten shots a round.'

'Or you can try saying something like: 'Watch out for those bushes on the left. I hope you don't go in there',' said Oliver.

'It's always wise to draw your opponent's attention to any hazard – even if he's nowhere near it,' said Gerald. 'Point out bunkers, trees and water even if they're playing in the other direction.'

'I once warned a chap about a huge bunker two fairways away,' said Oliver. 'He hit his next shot straight into it. Amazing. Until I mentioned it he couldn't have done it if he'd tried.'

This made good sense to me. I had already noticed that the best way to hit something was to try to avoid it and the best way to miss something was to aim straight at it. I had, for example, discovered that if a bunker lay between my ball and the green then I would be most likely to miss the bunker if I aimed directly at it and tried to knock my ball straight into the sand. This, I had found, worked for any hazard and when I thought about it, it made a great deal of sense. I did, after all, find it virtually impossible to hit a green when aiming for it so what chance would there be of my deliberately hitting something much smaller – such as a bunker?

'If you hit a good shot give your opponent some ridiculously complicated instructions on how to replicate your success,' said Gerald. 'I once hit a real fluke on the third at Bilbury Golf Club. It's a short hole where the green is surrounded by water and I nearly always go into the lake. On the rare occasions when I have managed to hit the green my ball has always rolled on and fallen into the lake on the far side of the green. I was so sure that I'd lose my ball that on this occasion I put down the oldest ball I'd got in my bag – it had two huge cuts in the cover and a flap was hanging loose – and just whacked it with a nine iron. It shot right up into the sky, landed on the green and stopped dead. The flap of loose cover was so big you could hear the ball whirring in the air. And it was the flap which stopped the ball rolling onwards into the lake, you see. The chap I was playing with didn't realise this and asked me how on earth I'd managed to stop the ball so quickly. I told him that I kept my left elbow bent, put all my weight on my left toes, kept my right shoulder down, gripped down the shaft an extra couple of inches and hit across the ball to give it sideways spin.'

'What happened?'

'He lost eight balls in the lake, took 97 for the first nine, threw his bag into the pond on the 12th, gave me the £50 quid we were playing for in cash and as far as I know never played again.'

'You can do that the other way round,' said Oliver. 'If your opponent plays a good shot ask him to explain how he did it. Ask him to show you the secret of his wonderfully smooth swing. Once they've tried to analyse how they hit a golf ball most people are lost. Look at all the pros who've tried too hard; the ones who have won a tournament and then spent the next few months poring over videos so that they can see exactly how they achieved their success. They end up not being able to hit the ball at all.'

'I always find it's useful to say something like 'That's a very interesting grip,' said Gerald. 'It makes them think about things; makes them look at their grip, probably for the first time. Introspection always heralds disaster.'

'And the beauty of it is that asking for advice makes you seem such a pleasant chap,' he added. 'How can anyone take offence when a playing partner flatters you and asks for your thoughts?'

'Are players allowed to give one another advice?' I enquired.

'Dodgy area,' said Simon

'If anyone complained I'd just tell them that the rules have been changed,' said Oliver. 'Actually, it's a bad idea to take any notice of advice anyway.'

'Why's that?' I asked.

'Golfers have a tendency to lie.'

'Oh, absolutely,' nodded Gerald. 'But remember that if you are asked for advice you only need to lie once.'

I frowned. 'I don't understand.'

'If you lie the first time you're asked for advice you won't ever need to lie again,' explained Gerald. 'Your opponent won't believe you. Even if you're telling the truth he'll be uncertain. He'll suspect that you might be double crossing him.'

'Another thing to remember is that you should never, ever bet on your own skills,' said Oliver. 'If you bet on yourself to do something you'll be putting yourself under pressure. Put the other guy under pressure instead.'

'If you're playing across water bet them that they can't clear it,' said Gerald. 'If they do it once, bet them that they can't do it again. If they do it twice, give up.'

'If you've got a bet on and your opponent is trying to hit his ball over a lake you should always try to persuade him to play safe,' said Oliver. 'Suggest that he plays short. Explain the dangers of playing the shot. Point out that you wouldn't try it and that he mustn't feel bad if he decides to take the easy option.'

'No one can resist a challenge like that,' said Gerald.

I didn't say anything. I was too busy trying to remember everything I'd been told.

'Ah, there's always lots left to learn,' sighed Gerald.

'We're always learning aren't we?' said Oliver.

'Absolutely,' agreed Gerald. 'Here's a little tip: in cold weather always take a hip flask with you but fill it with warm black tea. No milk.'

'What on earth for?' I asked.

'Makes your opponent think you're getting pissed,' said Gerald. 'He'll probably want to up the bets after a few holes. Especially if you start stumbling around and missing the ball a few times where it doesn't matter too much.'

'If you're playing for money make sure that you remind him of the sums involved at every available opportunity,' added Oliver.

'It helps to keep the pressure up,' explained Gerald.

'And wear a black arm band,' suggested Oliver. 'But don't say why.'

'What on earth for?' I asked.

'If anyone asks you why you're wearing it just tell them you'd rather not say because you don't want to spoil the mood of the day.'

'But they'll think...'

'Exactly, they'll think you've lost someone close to you. They'll respect you for turning up to play. They'll feel sorry for you.'

'Always the first step down the slippery slope towards losing,' said Gerald.

'When you turn up on the first tee, have a cough,' said Oliver. 'Cough three or four times. Then for the rest of the round, when they've got their ball teed up put your hand over your mouth and make it clear that you're making a great effort not to cough. You never actually cough again, of course. But they'll be waiting for the cough that never comes.'

'Of course you have to watch out because the chances are the other chap will be trying all his tricks on you,' said Gerald, with a warning shake of the index finger of his left hand . 'So, for example, never accept a ball from your opponent. Even if it looks brand new and he unwraps it in front of your eyes.'

'Why on earth not?'

'It might be soaked in vinegar,' said Oliver. 'Old trick. Turns the ball into a stone. Hit it and it will wreck your joints, your back, your club and your round.'

'And talking of balls, always use what look like brand new ones,' said Gerald. 'Nice psychological trick.'

'But brand new balls are ridiculously expensive,' I protested.

'You don't actually use brand new balls,' said Oliver patiently. 'Just give some of your old balls a scrub and then wrap them up in wrappers and boxes you've picked out of the rubbish bins around the course.'

'If you know any sexy young things get them to walk round with you,' said Gerald. 'Preferably in the shortest skirt and tightest jumper they've got.'

'Bound to put people off,' said Oliver.

'I once beat an assistant professional by getting my niece to caddy for me,' said Gerald. 'He couldn't take his eyes off her. I won five and four.'

'Never trust opponents who say they always play with the same numbered ball,' said Gerald. 'Too easy for them to do a Goldfinger and just slip another ball down into the rough or onto the fairway.'

'Never trust anyone who doesn't want help looking for his ball in the rough,' said Gerald.

'Mind you, I did know a chap who let people look for his ball then, when they'd found one he would just pick it up, pocket it and say it wasn't his,' said Oliver.

'I once knew a chap who always played for the rough,' said Simon. 'He once admitted that he preferred playing from off the fairway because no one could see what he was doing.'

'If your ball is in the rough you can adjust your lie while

pretending to check that the ball is yours,' said Gerald. 'Popping a ball on a nice tuft of grass in the rough is like teeing it up. Much better than having to play it off thin fairway grass that has been cut too short.'

'Watch out for people who use the old Cobb wedge,' said Gerald.

'Cobb wedge?' I said, puzzled. 'What's that?'

'A boot,' said Oliver. 'Named after the famous London bootmakers.'

'Someone who kicks his ball into a better position is using the Cobb wedge,' said Gerald.

'That's cheating,' said Oliver, wagging a warning finger. 'Against the rules – even our rules.' He paused. 'Well most of the time,' he added after exchanging glances with Gerald.

'And learn the rules of golf,' Gerald told me firmly. 'One or two of them anyway. No normal human being can possibly know all the rules so learn a few rules very well and you'll be well ahead of everyone else.'

'You don't have to be absolutely 100% accurate,' Oliver assured me. 'The important thing is only that you are convincing. And that people believe you.'

'And never argue about rules when you're in the clubhouse,' warned Gerald. 'Or some blighter will potter off and fetch a copy of the rule book or ring up the R&A and get a ruling.'

'If you keep your pontificating for the course you're pretty safe,' said Oliver. 'When you get back to the clubhouse you can always insist that they've misremembered and are misquoting you.'

'And, as you've learned, remember to watch out for the chap who doesn't add up very well,' added Simon finally. 'There are lots of golfers who ignore the shots they don't like.'

'Chap I knew never took more than five however many times he hit the ball,' said Oliver. 'He would walk off the green after losing three balls and hacking away from one side of the fairway to the other and announce: 'I'll put myself down for a five on that hole.' He would then pull out his card and give himself a five. 'I think that's pretty fair,' he would add, as he put the card back into his trouser pocket.

'I think I've played with him,' I said drily. 'Quite a few times.'

Chapter Eleven
'You'll Be Doing Me A Real Favour.'

Gerald and Oliver had just come back from a golfing holiday. In order to allay feelings of guilt they had bought each other the trip as a Christmas present some months earlier. They were both looking tanned and healthy, though I suspected that both of them had put on a little weight.

'What did you do?' asked Simon, as we all sat around drinking the club's claret. We'd spent the morning losing golf balls, had had a splendid lunch and were now enjoying ourselves doing nothing much. 'Lessons? Exercises? Did they video your swing and play it back for you?'

'Oh, we didn't go on one of those holidays,' replied Oliver, putting all the emphasis on the penultimate word. 'Ours was a much simpler affair. Up every morning at 8.30 am. Large cooked breakfast – mainly fat and cholesterol with a couple of tomatoes thrown on top to add colour – and then a round of golf. After the morning's golf we had a huge lunch, usually steak and chips decorated with a token piece of broccoli, and a couple of bottles of the local plonk.'

'After lunch we played golf again,' said Gerald. 'Then a five course dinner and another couple of bottles of wine followed by some of the local brandy.'

'Then we watched the golf channel on TV and went to bed,' finished Oliver. 'Simple sort of holiday.'

'Pretty good for people who like golf,' said Simon.

'Oh, people who didn't like golf probably wouldn't have gone too much on it,' admitted Oliver. 'Not for more than a couple of days anyway.'

'How long were you there?'

'Two weeks,' answered Gerald. He looked around the lounge. 'Nice to be back, though,' he said. He looked around again. 'Being back reminds me how many nutters there are here.'

'Nutters? What do you mean?' demanded Simon. 'Are you impugning the mental health of our fellow members?'

'You'll find more fruitcakes here than in any railway station buffet,' said Gerald. 'I sometimes wish I was a writer. You wouldn't have to go out into the world to find people to write about. You could get plenty of material just sitting here.'

At the time I thought it was the claret talking. The club's claret, which is excellent and was apparently discovered by the wine committee on a fact finding mission to Bordeaux in the late 1980s, seems to have a mind and a voice of its own.

But after reflection I realised that Gerald was right. In my first few months as a member of the golf club I met more 'eccentrics' and 'characters' than one would expect to meet in a decade of normal life.

(People who have no money and who lose their minds or behave curiously are invariably dismissed as 'potty' and are tranquillised or sedated before being tucked away out of sight in hostels; forced to spend their days wandering the streets, sheltering in public libraries or riding round and round on public transport. People who have enough money to afford to play golf and behave strangely are simply regarded as 'eccentrics' or 'characters' and will, as long as their money holds out, usually manage to escape the clutches of those modern day Bedlam guards: the mental health nurses and social workers.)

Just two days later events were set in motion which led to my meeting four of the most extraordinary characters I'd ever come across.

* * *

I was standing at the bar ordering a dish of steak and kidney pudding and a glass of red wine when someone I recognised but did not know appeared beside me. He was tall, immaculately dressed in a blue blazer, grey flannels, white shirt, regimental tie and well-shined black shoes. His white hair was arranged in what I believe ladies and hairdressers refer to as a 'bouffant' style, (a hairstyle popularised by male television presenters anxious to give themselves an extra inch or two in height) and he brought with him a cloud of aftershave. He had a way of moving that didn't seem to involve legs or feet. P.G.Wodehouse famously described Bertie Wooster's butler as shimmering into position and the word describes the form of motion better than any other I can think of.

'You're new aren't you?' he asked, peering at me as though he were a doctor and I were a rash.

I nodded, confirmed that I was and tried, unsuccessfully, to stifle a cough. The aftershave he was wearing was rather pungent.

'You're the plumber,' he said. It wasn't a question, it was a statement.

'Well, actually...' I began. It was a conversation I was getting so tired of that I had been thinking of giving up my job at the paper and training as a plumber. I thought it would probably be easier to become a plumber than to convince people that I wasn't one. And I was getting fed up with the fact that people *wanted* me to be a plumber. People who had greeted me with great enthusiasm invariably seemed to lose interest in me when they learned that I was a journalist.

'Rupert,' he said. 'Vice-president in charge of external relations.' He reached into a side pocket of his blazer and pulled out a small black leather card case. He took a card from the case and handed it to me. I examined it. It contained his name, the name of our golf club and the words 'vice-president in charge of external relations'.

'Delighted to meet you,' I said, bowing very slightly.

He didn't speak but the hand which had given me the card remained stretched out. I assumed he was expecting me to reciprocate. 'I'm afraid I don't think I have a card with me,' I said. I patted my trouser pockets as though wondering if I might find a card case. Naturally, as I had known it would be, my patting was unproductive. I told him my name. His hand remained outstretched. I looked down at it, wondering whether he'd perhaps simply forgotten it was still there.

'My card, please,' he said.

'Oh yes,' I said, feeling rather embarrassed. I wasn't up with modern visiting card etiquette. I handed him back his card which he carefully put back into the card case. He then put the case back into his jacket pocket. He checked to make sure that the flap on his pocket was hanging neatly, smoothed the cloth of his jacket and drew his lips back to show me two rows of capped teeth in what I suspect he would have described as a 'winning smile'.

'Are you settling in well?' he enquired.

I thanked him and told him that I was. The barman brought my steak and kidney pudding and my glass of red wine.

'Ah, I see you like the simple fare,' said Rupert. 'You prefer the pudding to the pie? They do good food here don't they? Do you eat here frequently? You do find the food satisfactory? What do you think of the puddings?'

I looked down and examined my lunch as though it was a surprise to see it there. 'Er sometimes, yes, almost always, often, very tasty, particularly good,' I mumbled. Other words dribbled out of my mouth but I can't remember what they were and they were of little or no consequence.

'I won't interrupt your luncheon,' said Rupert. 'But we must get to know one another a little better sometime.' He scratched his chin thoughtfully and then raised the finger with which he had scratched as though an idea had come to him. 'It's the Captain's Cup next Saturday,' he said. 'Will you be free?'

To put this simple sounding invitation into perspective it is necessary to insert here a couple of footnotes. One about the Captain's Cup and the other about Rupert.

First, the Captain's Cup.

Our club has a number of annual championships. It is, says Gerald, a way of ensuring that almost everyone who wants to win something will end the year with something atrociously ugly in silver plate balanced on their mantelpiece. There are (and this is apparently just a coincidence) exactly the same number of major tournaments as there are members of the club's management committee. But the Captain's Cup is the most prestigious of the club's competitions. The trophy itself, is a masterpiece of overstatement; a tarnished extravaganza of Edwardian metalwork; a confection of scrolls, whorls and nymphs garlanded in lilies. Two amply proportioned maidens, hair streaming down their backs, stretch upwards, their bodies uncomfortably arched so that they may serve as handles. Together they support a bowl decorated with engraved names and dates. The cup is impossible to clean properly, though the winners invariably spend many hours working at it with silver polish. One exuberant winner attempted to clean the twiddlier of the twiddly bits with an old toothbrush but the implement he chose was hard-bristled and the scratches which his effort wrought can still be seen. The Captain's Cup is an invitation only event. No one I knew had ever played in it.

Second, Rupert.

Rupert was, at the time, chairman of the club's Competitions Committee and regarded as a potent force in club politics. When Prince Andrew had visited the club on one of his regular annual golf course crawls, Rupert had been a member of the party which had met the Royal golfer as he had stepped out of the Royal helicopter, one of the members he had had lunch with and one of the three representatives of the club chosen to accompany the Royal golfer around our humble course. This was a tribute to Rupert's power within the club for several hundred members had fought hard for months for the right to boast of having played alongside the Prince. The behind-the-scenes trickery which had led to such success for Rupert had been of a quality that would have impressed Machiavelli himself. (In the end the Prince had had to leave after seven holes in order to make a business appointment on a yacht in the Seychelles, but to those who care about these things even seven holes played with a real Prince are very welcome.)

* * *

I had, at the time of Rupert's invitation, played no more than a few dozen rounds of golf and the quality of my golf was still something of a curate's egg.

It was clear, to me at least, that I would, in due course, be as good a golfer as ever lived. But, I still had one foot on the floor and I didn't think I was as yet quite up to tournament standard.

'I'm not, er, sure,' I stuttered. 'I, er, well, er, am not terribly...been playing very long, you know.'

My power of speech seemed to have deserted me.

'It'll be valuable experience for you,' said Rupert smoothly.

I still hesitated.

'You'll be doing me a real favour,' he murmured.

'Oh.' I said. I was flattered. I wondered if he had perhaps heard about the seven iron shot I'd played earlier that week. From the moment I'd hit the ball I'd known it was going to be a good shot. The ball had landed no more than thirty feet from the pin and although it had rolled back a few feet into the grassy fringe at the front of the green, it had still, I thought, been a memorable looking shot.

'Absolutely. Start time is 9.30 am. I'll meet you on the first tee.'

I could hardly say 'no' to such a request from such an important member of the club. I nodded, said how delighted I would be and bowed my head as he left as one might do after receiving a commendation from royalty. I was so flustered that I don't remember much about the next fifteen minutes but when I next looked down the steak and kidney pudding was gone and so was the wine.

* * *

I spent the next three days standing on the practice ground hitting an endless series of elderly golf balls into various parts of the distance.

These days driving ranges have taken the fun out of practice. Golfers just stand in little cubicles with a bucket of balls and a club. They drag the next ball into position so they don't have to move their feet. And then: ping, ping, ping. They hardly bother to look up to see where the ball has landed before they line up the next one. They have no need to look where every ball lands because a man in an armoured tractor drives around every so often and rakes them all up.

We don't have a driving range at our club and nor do we have a proper practice ground. There is a practice putting green, of course, and a small area has been set aside for chipping and bunker work but for longer irons and woods it's necessary to walk a couple of hundred yards to what is for all practical purposes a field. The grass is cut occasionally, but it's still pretty much just a field.

I had to use my own balls (mostly battered, scarred and decorated with corporate logos) and I had to watch exactly how far I hit them (and in what direction) because I had to find them afterwards. Each time I ran out of balls to hit I went and picked them all up myself; using a sand iron to scoop the balls off the ground and into a shopping bag I carried. During those three days I got very good at picking up golf balls. Scooping balls up with a sand iron was, I suspect, the smoothest, most reliable shot in my repertoire. I even perfected a way to bounce a ball out of long grass using a nine iron with the blade laid very flat.

'I don't approve of practising,' Gerald always insisted. He thought of practising as cheating. But I put his pessimistic viewpoint aside and I practised. I practised on the putting green. I practised chipping. I practised bunker shots. But, most of all, I practised my long irons and my driving. Professionals say, quite rightly, that 'driving is for show and putting is for dough'. But I wasn't playing for dough – I was playing for show. I wanted to impress Rupert and I was determined not to let myself down in my first tournament.

* * *

When I walked onto the first tee at 9.29 am the following Saturday morning the first thing I noticed was that there were three other men standing there with Rupert. I didn't know any of them personally but I recognised them all.

The presence of three others seemed odd to me because according to my maths this meant that there would be five of us playing. All four of them already had drivers in their hands and although the previous four were no more than fifty or sixty yards down the fairway my prospective playing partners were already loosening up stiff muscles with some preliminary swings.

The three men were, I knew, called Humphrey, Nigel and Alfred. Humphrey was the only one of the three I had met. He was in his mid sixties, though he looked older, and still worked as an insurance salesman, though I believe he called himself a 'Malfortune and Unexpected Incident Compensation Consultant'. He was a cautious, thoughtful man. We had occasionally exchanged criticisms of the weather while standing at the bar, and I had watched him tee off once or twice while sitting on the terrace. He had an interesting style, popular with many men of his age. He used a three wood off the tee but his backswing never lifted the club above waist level. This limited the distance he could hit the ball but helped ensure that it rarely landed anywhere but on short grass. He once told me that his philosophy was to keep it short and straight and never take more than two putts. 'Keep it short, keep it straight and putt like a demon,' were his motto. Most memorably of all he had, within days of my joining the club, succeeded in selling me a 'Trophy Insurance' policy.

'If you win a tournament you'll get to take the trophy home with you,' he told me. 'But in the excitement you'll probably not think about the possibly disastrous consequences that could be the downside of your success.'

He had explained to me that if a trophy were to be stolen while in my possession the club would hold me responsible but that my household insurance would probably not cover the loss. 'Just imagine the consequences,' he'd told me. 'The intrinsic value of a major trophy can be substantial. A trophy at one club I know of has been valued at £37,500.' Having created the fear in my mind Humphrey had, naturally, offered me the palliative. 'For just £29.99 a year I can give you complete peace of mind,' he had told me. I'd written out a cheque there and then and had gone home a very relieved man. Humphrey had subsequently sold me insurance cover to protect me against the loss of my clubs, insurance against the cost of all the drinks I would have to buy if I scored a hole in one and insurance against accidentally hitting an innocent passer-by, motorist or house with a golf ball I had struck. Walter, the club professional had sold me a similar policy, but although he was adept at selling pink jumpers and blue golf bags he was not in Humphrey's class when it came to selling insurance. Humphrey had been far more reassuring.

Whenever I saw Humphrey I always felt slightly nervous, knowing that he was almost certain to find something new for me to worry about. This anxiety was alleviated only by the confident feeling that whatever new worry Humphrey was able to alert me to he would also be able to offer me a cure.

Although I had never met nor spoken to the other two I felt I knew them quite well. To say that I was surprised to see them playing together was a bit like saying that I would have been surprised to see Saddam Hussein and George Bush teeing up alongside one another.

I suspect that most clubs contain members who have had minor feuds or disagreements. But within days of joining my club I had noticed that there were two members who seemed to put a good deal of effort into avoiding one another. There had, it seemed, been a rather more than usual run-of-the-mill falling out.

I asked Oliver about it one day.

'They used to be great chums,' explained Oliver. 'Played golf together twice a week for years. They even went on golfing holidays together every winter.'

'What happened?' I asked. It seemed difficult to believe that two players with such obvious antipathy towards one another could have ever been friends.

'Nigel got a hole in one,' interrupted Oliver. 'Short hole, of course. I didn't see it myself but it was, so they say, a beautiful shot which landed just on the front of the green and curled round slightly right to left to fall neatly into the cup. Alfred, his playing partner as usual, hit a good shot too. A nice five iron which landed about eight feet from the pin. Nigel, being a modest sort of fellow, didn't make a great fuss about his achievement. He was bursting with excitement but thought he'd just quietly mention it when they came to mark their cards at the end of the hole. He wasn't entirely sure whether Alfred hadn't seen the hole in one or was just teasing him – pretending not to have seen it.

When they got to the green Alfred concentrated really hard on his putt. He didn't score a great many birdies so for him this was a special moment; a real, genuine birdie opportunity. He spent ages sizing things up. Eventually, he crouched over the putt. Stayed there for hours. Then hit it and missed the hole by about one foot to the left and eight feet too far. Terrible putt. He was so shaken that he took four more and just managed to salvage a triple bogey. At the end of the hole Alfred turned to Nigel and said: 'What did you get?'

'Nigel, who had been waiting for this moment, coughed and, doing his very best to sound nonchalant, replied: 'One."

'Alfred grunted. 'Your hole then,' he said."

"I got a hole in one,' said Nigel, in case Alfred hadn't quite understood.'

"I heard you,' said Alfred. 'You won the hole. Don't make a big fuss about it."

'They finished the round together but as they walked off the 18th Nigel turned to Alfred and said: 'I will never, ever speak to you again."

And, said Oliver, he hasn't. I was about to find out if Oliver was right.

* * *

Nigel was wearing a brown pullover, brown corduroy trousers and a green and yellow checked cap. Alfred was wearing a pair of charcoal grey trousers with a fine chalk stripe and a matching waistcoat and, rather incongruously, a pair of white and red sports shoes and a purple bobble hat. Despite the fact that it was a beautiful morning and there wasn't a cloud in the sky Humphrey was wearing a blue waterproof jacket and matching blue waterproof trousers. The hood of his jacket was down but ready for action. Humphrey was not a man to take chances.

'What on earth have you got those for? demanded Rupert. He was wearing a bright pink sweater, embroidered with a small tortoise over the left breast, a pair of green tartan trousers and a pair of white and brown golf shoes in what is known as the correspondent style. (The word 'correspondent' refers, I had once been assured by Oliver, not to the sort of superior journalist who, like Boot of Scoop fame reports from some foreign capital, but to the sort of person likely to be named as the third party in a divorce action.)

I removed my bag from my shoulder and looked around. 'Got what for?' I asked him, truly puzzled.

'I don't need your clubs you idiot,' Rupert hissed. 'I've got my own.'

'Shouldn't we have a bag each?' I asked. I knew that although the committee had no objection to players sharing balls they did frown on players sharing clubs. This didn't make an awful lot of sense to me but I had grown accustomed to the fact that in the world of golf quite a lot of things don't make an awful lot of sense.

'You don't need those,' muttered Rupert, indicating my clubs with a disdainful wave of a hand, at the same time turning away from his three companions so that they would not hear. 'I'm only allowed fourteen clubs. It's against the rules to carry any more.'

I am rather slow-witted sometimes. The truth still didn't dawn on me. 'I know that,' I replied. 'But...'

Rupert took me by the shoulder and moved me aside a few feet. 'You're caddying for me,' he said. 'You do know that don't you?'

I had, of course, had no idea that Rupert had invited me to be his caddy. To say that I felt embarrassed would have been a dramatic understatement. There is no word in the English language which adequately describes the way I felt. 'Right,' I said, nodding furiously. 'Sorry. Of course I knew that,' I lied. 'I just thought you might like to have some extra clubs.' I waved a hand about helplessly. 'Spares. In case you lose some, or break a few.'

'Take your damned clubs back to the clubhouse,' hissed Rupert. He looked around. Nigel was bending down sticking a red plastic tee into to the turf. 'Shan't be a moment,' Rupert called out brightly. 'Just clearing up a misunderstanding with my caddy.' He turned back to me. 'You can take those back to the clubhouse,' he told me loudly. 'I'll use this set today.'

Blushing loudly I hurried back to the clubhouse. Behind me I heard Rupert explaining that I was new and had not realised that he would be taking the set of clubs he had chosen to use to the tee himself. 'Well-meaning fellow,' I heard him say. 'But not the brightest of God's creatures.' I think I heard him add something about employing me only because he felt sorry for me and, although I may be wrong about this, I fancied that I heard the word 'plumber' somewhere in the monologue.

* * *

I had never seen Rupert play golf and I had assumed, quite wrongly as it turned out, that someone of such stature in the club must be a skilful and accomplished player. This was not the case. The only positive thing you could say about Rupert's golf game was that there were no weaknesses. There was no part of his game that let him down.

Unfortunately, this was the case only because Rupert's game was uniformly bad. Just as there were no weaknesses so, by the same token, there were no strengths.

From the tee his drives were so wayward that I soon decided that the safest place to stand would have been directly in front of him if that had been allowed. That was the only place where a bystander could guarantee not to be hit by the ball.

Rupert's drives rarely hit the fairways at all and although he inevitably played a high proportion of his shots from the rough and from the bunkers he had not, it seemed, acquired any special skills in helping his ball to progress from these hazards.

On the green, Rupert's putting was both wayward and timid and his ball, like France and America, always seemed to be just one revolution short of success and happiness. It is not often that one sees a golfer consistently miss putts which are less than twelve inches long and on the first green, when Rupert took three from less than a yard, I was reminded of a match I had played with Gerald and Oliver.

'How many did you take?' Gerald had asked Oliver as we had all marked one another's cards. 'It would have been a fifteen if that one had gone in,' replied Oliver who was having a day which would have inspired a less committed enthusiast to resign his golf club membership and take up something less taxing. 'Good heavens,' said Gerald. 'How did you manage that?' 'A good drive and three or four good iron shots,' said Oliver. 'It was that putt I missed coming back that spoilt things. If that had gone in I would have got down in fifteen.'

Naturally, however, despite the shortcomings in his game, Rupert was, like virtually every golfer on the planet, secretly and quietly convinced that if the gods would but look on him with more generosity in their hearts, he would be able to carve a successful career as a tournament professional. 'The only difference between me and Jack Nicklaus,' he said as we eventually left the first green where he had tackled putts from virtually every possible angle, 'is that Nicklaus doesn't have to worry about earning a living selling houses. If I had the time to play more often – and a little of his luck – I would be the one with the living room full of ugly silverware.'

By the end of the second hole it was clear that Rupert was not playing at his best and was becoming increasingly irritable.

When I had told my usual playing partners of my good fortune in being invited to (as I thought) play in the Captain's Cup, Gerald had irreverently described my benefactor as suffering from Irritable Person Syndrome and although, generally speaking, I thought this a little unfair I had to admit that there were moments when the description seemed to fit. The problem was that as the day went on the moments were beginning to run together and turn into periods.

In addition, the unspoken but almost tangible antipathy between Nigel and Alfred meant that the game was being played in the sort of atmosphere most commonly associated with family Christmases and a certain type of wedding.

* * *

At the seventh hole the fairway runs alongside a road and a lorry driver who had parked in a lay-by to eat his sandwiches watched us as we made our way, rather erratically, towards the green.

'Can't you move that fellow along?' Rupert demanded.

'Which fellow?'

'The lorry driver. He's watching me.'

'He's eating his lunch,' I said. 'I don't think I can move him along. He's parked. He's not doing anything illegal.'

'He's intruding upon my privacy. It's harassment,' complained Rupert.

I tried to explain again that the lorry driver was merely amusing himself while he ate his lunch. I did not mention, because it did not seem necessary, that even though I could only see his top half he seemed to be a substantial fellow. I long ago decided not to pick fights with edentulous men who shave their heads and have their forearms decorated with tattoos. There are no logical reasons for this although I suppose that fear and self-preservation are acceptable as reasons go and I am old enough to regard fear as a virtue rather than a weakness.

'You're afraid of him,' said Rupert scornfully.

'You're right,' I nodded. 'And I think he's got a dog in the cab with him. I'm sure I heard something bark.'

'It's probably just a poodle,' said Rupert. 'One of those ornamental things with a red collar round its neck.' He took a huge swing at his ball, which was lying half buried in thick grass, and successfully moved it nearly a foot, though not, sadly, in the direction of the green.

'I don't think he's the sort of chap to have a poodle,' I said. 'He looks more like an Alsatian or a Dobermann fellow. Possibly a Pit Bull terrier.' I adjusted the bag on my shoulder. 'Anyway,' I said, 'you must be used to playing in front of an audience. When you played with Prince Andrew there were at least a dozen blokes walking around with you. Great big chaps who all seemed to have hearing problems.'

'They weren't watching the golf,' said Rupert. 'They were checking to make sure that there weren't any terrorists hiding behind trees. They were just there to protect us.'

I liked the royal use of the word 'us', suggesting that the men from Special Branch were there as much to protect Rupert as to protect Prince Andrew, but I didn't say anything about it.

'Professionals perform well before an audience,' Rupert said, 'only because they are primarily entertainers. Exhibitionists. Show-offs. But I consider myself more an artist. How do you think that sensitive chap who cut off his ear would have managed if he had looked up and seen a cluster of small children watching him dip his brush in the ochre?'

'Van Gogh,' I said. It did occur to me to point out that Rupert would not have much chance of building a career as a tournament professional, playing in front of crowds of thousands, if he couldn't cope with a lorry driver idly peering over the hedge at him. But I didn't mention that either.

'Who?'

'The chap who cut off his ear,' I said. 'He was called Van Gogh.'

'I know that,' said Rupert, giving another display of irritability.

'Foreign I expect.' He hit a seven iron another three yards though at least this time the ball ended up closer to the green at the end of the shot than it had been at the start of it. 'Is that five or six I've taken?'

'Eleven.'

'It can't possibly be.'

It is well known to doctors that smokers and drinkers, when asked about their habits, always halve what they say they use. The fellow who smokes 60 a day will say he smokes 30. The chap who drinks a bottle of wine a day will say he occasionally drinks a couple of glasses with his dinner. Some golfers are the same. I'm not being critical about this. There is nothing particularly bad about it. But it is a fact. Some golfers automatically adjust their score. Naturally, like smokers and drinkers, the totals are always adjusted downwards. It becomes such a habit that they often don't even know they're doing it. If you told them they were cheating they'd be shocked. Rupert was one of the golfers who are most ruthless in adjusting their scores.

'It's eleven,' I told him again. 'If you are counting all the times you hit the ball. You missed it twice but I didn't think you'd want to bother with those.'

'You don't have to sound so damned pleased about it.'

'I'm not pleased about it,' I protested. I was getting a little fed-up with Rupert's patronising and arrogant tone. 'You asked me how many shots you'd taken and I told you.'

'Not that I care,' said Rupert, suddenly changing his tune. 'It's just a game after all.' I nearly fainted when I heard this. Out of Rupert's mouth it sounded like blasphemy.

* * *

If Rupert's behaviour merited the adjective 'irritable' it is difficult to know how best to describe Nigel and Alfred. They hated one another so much that it quickly became clear that the failure of one to succeed would please the other far more than his own success. Whoever had selected Nigel and Alfred for the same quartet in the Captain's Cup must have been inspired by a strong sense of mischief-making.

On the first tee Nigel pulled his tee shot into a patch of bracken about a hundred and twenty yards away from the tee and approximately twenty yards from the fairway.

'Tell him that even for him that was a pathetic drive,' Alfred told me. As the only caddy in the bunch he had clearly decided that I was lowly enough to be appointed go-between for the duration of the match.

'Tell him that if I was him I'd wait until I'd hit my drive before I started making rude comments about other people's drives,' replied Nigel. He then watched with unconcealed delight as Alfred sliced his tee shot into a thick patch of gorse and brambles.

On the first green the two of them almost came to blows.

'He doesn't want me to hole that does he?' Nigel asked me, waving his putter towards his ball which was about eighteen inches from the hole.

'The competition is, strictly speaking, played according to medal play,' Rupert quietly reminded him.

Nigel glared at him. 'I wasn't talking to you,' he snarled.

'If he was talking to me then the answer is 'No',' said Alfred. 'I don't want him to hole that putt.'

Nigel bent down, picked up his ball and set off towards the next tee, showing no interest in the other three players.

'Foul. Tell him he loses the hole. He's disqualified. He's penalised two strokes for touching the ball!' I turned round and saw Alfred, now frothing at the mouth, pointing first to the hole and then to Nigel.

Nigel, hearing this, turned. 'Ask him what the devil he's on about,' he said to me. 'He said he didn't want me to hole it.'

'Ha!' said Alfred. 'Tell him I didn't want him to hole it because I wanted him to miss. But that didn't mean I gave him permission to pick up.'

Feeling a bit like a translator at a cold war summit meeting I repeated this to Nigel.

'Tell him that was a dirty trick,' said Nigel. 'Just what I'd expect of him.' He spat out the words as though it pained him to have them in his mouth. He then walked back towards the hole, replaced his ball, though this time no more than six inches away from the hole, and tapped it in. 'Ask him if he's satisfied now,' he snarled.

Alfred wasn't satisfied and insisted that he intended to report the whole incident and the question of deciding on an appropriate punishment to the match referee. He would, he told us, be calling us all as witnesses.

* * *

'It's your job to encourage me,' complained Rupert as we rather painfully made our way along the eighth fairway. 'You have to give me confidence.'

'Sorry,' I said. 'Two holes ago, when I told you not to worry too much about it when you took six getting out of that fairway bunker, you told me to shut up and just give you the clubs.'

'I was feeling edgy,' said Rupert. 'As a caddy you're supposed to understand that. Try and give me self-belief.' He held out a hand.

'What do you want?' I asked him.

'My driver,' he said.

'Are you sure?'

'Yes. I'm sure. Why?'

'Because the last three times you've used a driver you've lost your ball.'

'I don't care,' said Rupert, a trace petulantly, I thought. 'I want my driver.'

'OK,' I said, pulling his driver out of the bag and handing it to him. 'But you should know that the ball you're playing is the last one in your bag.'

'Making sure I had enough balls was your job!' complained Rupert.

'You packed the bag,' I reminded him. 'Anyway, when we started I counted the clubs and the balls you'd got. We started with 14 clubs and 24 balls. I thought it would be enough of both.'

'How many have I lost?' he asked.

'One club and 23 balls,' I replied. 'Your four iron is in a pond about half a mile back. I have no idea where the balls are. But that's why you've only got that one left.'

Rupert sighed and looked at me rather searchingly, as though trying to decide whether I might have been stealing his balls. 'Heaven knows where they've all gone,' he said. 'I haven't played that badly.' He swished his driver to and fro and then handed it back to me. 'I think my game has been pretty good, generally speaking. Don't you agree?'

'Well, sort of, I suppose,' I agreed, rather half-heartedly.

He stood back from the ball. 'Give me a seven iron,' he said. 'What do mean 'sort of'? What have I done wrong?' he demanded. 'Tell me!'

'You've been a little bit wayward,' I said. 'From time to time,' I added over-generously.

'Everyone hits the rough occasionally,' protested Rupert. 'Even the professionals. Look at Severiano Ballesteros!'

'But the pros do hit it further,' I pointed out. 'On the last hole you only hit your drive about fifty yards and it still went into a bush. Mr Ballesteros could hit it further than that if he used the bag to hit the ball.'

'Distance isn't everything,' responded Rupert immediately. 'Besides, that wasn't my fault!' he said, rather angrily. 'That bush was standing all by itself. It was in a perfectly clear piece of ground. I was just unlucky that it got in the way of my ball.'

'The bush was in the rough,' I corrected him.

'It wasn't really rough,' insisted Rupert. 'Not very rough.'

'It was rough,' I muttered. 'The grass we were standing in was so deep I couldn't see my feet.'

'I feel terrible now,' said Rupert.

'You have to think positive,' I told him.

'I am,' he said, settling down over the ball. 'Thanks to you I'm positive that this ball is going straight out of bounds.' He swung and missed the ball. 'Damn,' he muttered. 'Is anyone looking?'

'No,' I told him. 'Everyone else is too busy cheating to take any notice of what you're doing.'

'They're cheating?'

'A bit.'

'That was just a practice swing,' said Rupert. 'It doesn't count.'

'OK,' I said. I really didn't care. I just wanted to get back to the clubhouse and order a glass of whatever the barman had got that contained the highest percentage of alcohol.

* * *

On the ninth tee Alfred was so disgusted with his drive that he ran towards the nearest tree and started attacking it with the three iron he'd used to play the shot. He didn't finish his attack until the other three had hit their drives. The tree seemed able to absorb Alfred's anger but by the time Alfred ran out of steam the bottom end of the shaft of the three iron was clearly bent.

This probably would not have mattered too much but for the fact that the three iron wasn't the first club Alfred had damaged. His driver, two iron, four iron, six iron and both sand wedges were now all showing noticeable signs of what might, I suppose, be loosely referred to as 'wear and tear' though I know others do call it 'fairway rage'.

It wouldn't have mattered at all if Alfred had either dumped the damaged club into a nearby waste bin or had dropped the damaged club back into his bag and forgotten about it.

And it wouldn't have mattered at all if Alfred hadn't been playing with someone who hated him more than he hated death itself and whose main reason for living was clearly to find opportunities to criticise him.

Since the number of clubs available to him was now becoming severely limited Alfred pulled out his three iron for his second shot. Given the identity of his playing partners this was what is known in polite circles as an error of judgement but usually referred to more colloquially as a cock-up.

'Ha!' cried Nigel, making no attempt to conceal his delight. 'Tell him that he's going to be disqualified for that!'

Since Nigel had a voice which, if it had been more commonly available would have made the invention of the mobile telephone superfluous, and since his declaration could, consequently, probably be heard several counties away it seemed unnecessary actually to go through with the business of passing on this message. So I didn't.

'Tell him! Tell him!' shouted Nigel.

Wearily, I passed the message on to Alfred who was determinedly pretending not to have heard it.

'Ask the stupid prat what the hell he's talking about,' said Alfred.

I passed this on. Rupert and Humphrey had now joined us.

'Tell the stupid pillock that if he knew anything about the rules of golf he would know that the stupid prat is talking about the fact that if you use a club which you've modified you get disqualified!'

I repeated this.

'Ask him what the hell he's talking about!' said Alfred. 'I haven't modified this club at all.'

'Yes you have!' crowed Nigel, so thrilled that he forgot himself and spoke directly to Alfred. 'You bent it when you hit that tree!'

'That's not a modification!' responded Alfred, with a sneer.

'"Tis! Tis! Tis! You'll get disqualified. You're out of the tournament.' Nigel danced a little jig of joy.

'"Tisn't! Tisn't! Tisn't!' insisted Alfred. 'I won't.'

I gazed in astonishment as these two grown men continued to snarl insults and accusations at one another.

'You're a cheat! You'll be exposed and humiliated!' said Nigel, bubbles of saliva at both corners of his mouth.

Silence.

Nigel repeated his accusation and his prediction.

Silence.

And then slowly, very slowly, Alfred's knees buckled and with a gracefulness that to my knowledge he had never shown before, he fell to the ground.

For a moment or two no one said anything. Even Nigel was unusually quiet.

'He's collapsed,' said Rupert, quietly.

'He's dead,' said Humphrey, with strange certainty.

'Don't be silly,' said Rupert. 'How can you tell?'

Humphrey was the first to move. He strode across the turf to where Alfred was lying, stooped down and felt for a pulse. 'He's dead,' he said a moment or two later. 'Massive heart attack would be my guess.' He stood up and shook his head sadly. 'He should have bought my 'Accidental Death On The Course' policy,' he said to no one in particular. He looked around, gazing at each of the other two in turn. 'Very reasonable premiums,' he said. 'Excellent cover for the bereaved spouse.'

'The bastard!' cried Nigel, now almost speechless with rage. 'He died so that I couldn't have him disqualified.'

'I don't think you can say that,' said Rupert. He paused and thought for a moment. 'Not with any certainty,' he added.

'What are we going to do with him?' asked Humphrey.

We all looked at Humphrey. None of us spoke.

'We can't leave him lying in the middle of the fairway,' Humphrey pointed out. 'It wouldn't matter so much if he was in the rough but for once he's found a really decent lie.' He looked first behind us to the tee, and then ahead of us to the green. 'He's lying just where a poor club player will land a decent drive,' he said.

'Humphrey is right,' said Nigel. 'The pillock will be a playing hazard if we leave him here.'

'I wonder if you can move your golf ball if it lands on a dead body?' Rupert asked no one in particular.

'I'm pretty sure you can,' said Humphrey. 'A dead body would be classified as a loose impediment.' He thought for a while. 'But either way I think we should move him.'

'Where to?' asked Nigel. 'If we take him back to the golf club we won't be able to finish our rounds and we'll all be disqualifying ourselves from the tournament.'

'We'll all be disqualified anyway,' said Rupert, paling as he realised the full extent of the disaster. 'Alfred was marking my card. I can't switch markers half way through the match.' He slammed the club he was holding (I think it was a five iron) against the turf and cursed roundly. 'This was my best chance of winning this tournament,' he complained.

'We aren't any of us going to win,' said Humphrey, with rare honesty.

'You don't know that,' protested Rupert. 'It's a handicap tournament. Last year the winner went round in 85 but had a net score of 61 after his handicap had been deducted.'

'We could just take the silly bastard back with us,' said Nigel. 'And pretend he died after we'd finished our rounds.'

Everyone looked at him. I was speechless. I couldn't believe they were treating Alfred's death so callously.

'We could,' insisted Nigel. He looked at Rupert. 'The plumber could carry him,' he said. 'If you carry your own clubs.'

'Er...I don't er...,' I began. I didn't fancy the idea of lugging a dead body around the golf course with me. Alfred was no Sumo wrestler but he was not a small man either.

'Splendid idea!' cried Rupert, full of enthusiasm. 'My caddy can play Alfred's shots for him and mark my card. Then as we walk off the 18th Alfred can suddenly collapse and die.' He looked around, grinning broadly, and rubbed his hands together.

'Make sure he signs your card before he dies,' said Nigel.

'Oh absolutely,' said Rupert. He took the bag I was carrying from me and swung it up onto his shoulder. 'What the hell have you got in here?' he demanded.

'Your clubs,' I told him. 'Your water, your spare sweaters, your towels...'

'It doesn't usually weigh this much,' complained Rupert.

'You usually use a trolley,' I pointed out.

'Has Alfred got any balls?' asked Rupert, cutting me short and pointing to the dead man's bag. 'Have a look in his bag, will you?'

I put my foot down at this. Robbing the dead rather reminded me of stories I'd heard of scavengers taking money, rings and gold teeth from the corpses of fallen soldiers on the battlefield.

'He doesn't need them now, does he?' said Rupert. He unzipped one of the compartments on Alfred's bag, rummaged around inside and brought out a handful of balls. 'These will do to start with,' he said. He zipped the compartment back up again and put Alfred's balls into his own bag.

'Who's going to pull Alfred's trolley?' asked Humphrey.

'My caddy can do that,' said Rupert, looking at me.

I stared at him, disbelievingly.

'You're not carrying my bag now,' he explained.

'I can't carry Alfred and pull his trolley!' I protested. I walked over to where Alfred was still slumped on the grass. I felt sorry for the dead man. He hadn't been a particularly pleasant fellow but I didn't like the way the others had ignored his demise and had thought only of themselves. An idea was already forming in my mind.

'Put your bag on Alfred's trolley,' Humphrey suggested to Rupert.

'That's a good idea,' agreed Rupert. He swung his bag off his shoulder and onto Alfred's trolley. With some difficulty he managed to strap his bag alongside Alfred's bag. 'It's very heavy now,' he complained.

'It will be,' said Nigel. 'You've got two bags on there.' He thought for a moment. 'There's a rubbish bin on the next tee,' he pointed out. 'When we get there see if there's anything in Alfred's bag that you can chuck out.'

'There's a group just moved onto the tee behind us,' said Humphrey. 'I think we should play on.' He pulled out a club and walked over to where his ball was lying. The others followed his example, splitting up and moving off to where their balls were lying (or, in the case of Rupert, to the patch of rough where he thought his ball had landed). I was left to pull Alfred to his feet, wrap my arm around his shoulders and stagger off down the fairway with him. His feet dragged behind, gouging lumps out of the turf as we went.

I got to the green behind Nigel and Humphrey but ahead of Rupert who arrived, huffing and puffing and cursing as he pulled his doubly laden trolley. I lay Alfred down on the grass beside the green and slumped down beside him. I was exhausted already and felt that if a doctor had looked at the two of us he would have had a job to decide which of us to resuscitate and which to bury.

'Can't I just dump Alfred's bag,' Rupert asked the others. 'This bloody trolley is unmanageable with two bags on it.'

'No!' insisted Humphrey. 'We can't go back without Alfred's bag. Remember Alfred is supposed to be still playing golf.'

Rupert moaned a bit but when he'd finished putting he rummaged around in Alfred's bag and pulled out everything he thought he could throw away. Two perfectly good jumpers, a set of waterproofs, some spare gloves and a large box of toffees all ended up stuffed into the waste bin on the next tee.

'Put me down for a five,' Rupert told me. 'You're scoring for me now.' He pulled out his own scorecard. 'What the hell shall I put down for Alfred?'

'Three,' I said.

'Never!' said Rupert.

'Three,' I insisted. I turned to the others. 'And if you want me to take Alfred to the 18th one of you is going to have to give me your trolley,' I said.

Nigel and Humphrey looked at me as if they were bank managers and I had asked them for a loan with no interest.

'Can't do that, old chap,' said Nigel.

'We need our trolleys,' said Humphrey.

'Then let's leave Alfred here and go back to the pavilion for help,' I said.

Eventually, with great reluctance, Humphrey agreed to let me use his trolley. Nigel refused point blank to let Alfred ride on his trolley even if I pulled it. We strapped Alfred onto Humphrey's trolley and put Humphrey's bag onto Nigel's trolley. Nigel and Humphrey agreed that they would take it in turns to pull the trolley carrying their two bags.

'No one is helping me and I'm pulling a trolley with two bags on it,' moaned Rupert, but no one took any notice of him.

'Shall I hit a ball for Alfred from the tee?' I asked, after the other three had driven off.

They looked at me.

'It'll look a bit strange if only three of us are playing,' I pointed out.

'He's right,' said Humphrey to the others. He looked at me. 'But you'll have to look a bit more like Alfred when you're playing,' he said. 'Put his bobble hat on.'

I protested about this but the others insisted and reluctantly I could see their point. I did have to look a bit like Alfred if I was going to be seen playing alongside the other three. And the bobble hat was pretty conspicuous. So I put the bobble hat on, pulled out Alfred's three wood, found a ball in his bag (Rupert had taken most of them but there were one or two left) and hit it.

We went on like this for several more holes and I enjoyed having a chance to play a little golf at last. Once I had adjusted his position and fastened him up tightly so that he didn't slide about Alfred was surprisingly easy to wheel along on the golf trolley. We did topple over sideways a couple of times but I seemed to have less trouble with him than Rupert, Nigel and Humphrey had pushing their trolleys containing two golf bags.

To begin with the biggest problem I had was that every time I wanted to play a shot I had to run over to where Rupert was, pull a club out of Alfred's bag, run back to where Alfred's ball was lying, play my shot and then return the club to the bag on the trolley Rupert was pushing. This became tedious after a while and I solved the problem by keeping a few irons stuffed down the front of Alfred's trousers. I decided that I could manage along the fairway with a five iron and a seven iron. On the tees and greens, of course, there were no problems because there we were all together and I could help myself without any problems.

As we played on I was delighted to see that Alfred was having far more success dead than he had ever had alive. On one of the short holes he even managed to get a hole in one. It was, they all agreed, the first hole in one he'd ever achieved. Nigel wasn't pleased but I didn't give him an option.

* * *

The first problem occurred on the 16th hole when Humphrey, who was about a hundred yards ahead of me, suddenly called my name and started jumping up and down and waving. I thought at first that he'd perhaps holed a long iron but after I had acknowledged his wave and shouted a what I hoped was appropriate 'Good shot' he carried on leaping up and down and waving and shouting. I noticed, too, that he was constantly looking over his shoulder as though something was worrying him. I left Alfred parked on his trolley in the rough (his drive, which had been rather wayward, had landed in some thick grass and if we hadn't been playing Rupert's rules would have been unplayable) and jogged up to Humphrey. He walked back to meet me as fast as his legs would carry him. He was still wearing his waterproofs and he made a strange sound when he moved. It was partly a rustle and partly a creak.

'It's the club captain,' wheezed Humphrey, gasping for breath and pouring sweat.

'What is?' I asked.

'Over there,' wheezed Humphrey, pointing behind him. 'He's making one of his tours of the golf course. What are we going to do?'

'Why don't you take your waterproofs off?' I asked him. 'You must be boiling.'

Humphrey looked at me as though I'd made an indecent suggestion. 'It might rain,' he told me, glancing up at the perfect blue sky above us. There wasn't a cloud to be seen for miles. 'The weather forecasters definitely said there would be rain.' He shrugged the weather forecast aside. 'I don't have time for that now,' he said. 'The captain will be here in five minutes.'

'Which captain?'

'The club captain.'

'What does he want?' I asked.

'The captain always walks round the course during the Captain's Cup,' explained Humphrey. 'It's a tradition.'

'Ah,' I said. I had been a member long enough to know that the word 'tradition' can be used to excuse any strange or otherwise inexplicable behaviour. There is never any point in questioning something described as a 'tradition'.

'He'll see Alfred's body and we'll be done for,' said Humphrey, who was now as close to panicking as a man can get without actually running amok.

'Don't worry!' I told Humphrey, trying to sound calmer than I felt. 'Everything will be fine.'

'How? Why? What are you going to do?' Humphrey still sounded panicky but my reassurance had calmed him a little.

'What's happening?' asked Nigel who had now hurried over to see what the problem was.

'Whatever it is can wait,' said Rupert, arriving a second or two after him. 'I've just spotted the captain. He's coming our way.'

'We know,' said Humphrey.

'Is the captain alone?' I asked.

'Yes.' replied Humphrey and Rupert simultaneously.

'He always does his walk by himself,' said Humphrey.

'It's a tradition,' said Rupert.

I gave thanks for tradition. 'The captain is that potty bloke who wears a pince-nez and walks with a limp?'

'Yes, yes, that's him.'

'He's about a hundred and ninety?'

'I don't think he's quite that old, but he's not the youngest member of the club,' agreed Humphrey.

'Does he know Alfred?'

'Only vaguely,' said Humphrey who wasn't wheezing so badly now.

'Fine,' I said. 'I'll keep Alfred's hat on for the time being and he'll think I'm him.'

'But what about the body?' demanded Humphrey. 'Shall we say that's you?'

I thought about this for a moment. 'No,' I said at last.

'This is going to all end badly,' cried Nigel. 'I knew we shouldn't have tried to do this. We'll all go prison. Pushing a body around on a golf trolley is bound to be against the law.'

'You three totter off and leave us alone,' I told Humphrey, Nigel and Rupert. 'Alfred and I will stay over here.'

'He'll wonder why there are five of us,' said Nigel.

'Tell him that I'm Alfred's caddy,' I said.

When they'd gone I unfastened the straps which held Alfred to the trolley and rolled the stiffening corpse off the trolley and into the thick grass. I then kicked Alfred's ball onto a tuft of grass and gave it a good whack with Alfred's five iron. Fortunately, it was a decent shot. Thanks to the grassy tee I'd used the ball soared high into the air, landed on the fairway about a hundred and fifty yards away and, with serendipity, rolled into a bunker where it temporarily disappeared from sight. Looking over to where the other three were now standing around staring at Humphrey's ball as though waiting for it to do something wonderful, I watched as the captain limped into view and headed towards them. I whipped Alfred's woolly hat from my head and crammed it onto his own head. I then rolled him over. The trolley was now empty, of course, though the few clubs which I had stuffed down Alfred's trousers were strewn on the grass. I could do nothing about the missing bag so I pushed the trolley off into the wilderness and half hid it behind a large gorse bush. The clubs I tossed into the grass beside it.

When I looked over to the others I could see that the captain had finished chatting to Nigel, Rupert and Humphrey and was now heading in my direction. I returned to where Alfred's corpse was lying, face down, on the grass. There was a rabbit hole nearby and in a flash of inspiration (and with some difficulty) I poked Alfred's stiffening arm down the rabbit hole. Exhausted by these exertions I knelt down beside Alfred and peered down the hole as though looking for something.

'Are you chaps OK?' asked a voice which could have come only from a man wearing a pince-nez. I looked up. A man with a pince-nez and an MCC tie was standing a few feet away.

'We're fine thank you,' I whispered, springing to my feet. 'I'm Alfred's caddy,' I whispered. 'He's just getting his ball out of a rabbit hole.'

'Ah, splendid,' said the captain. He peered across to where Alfred was stretched out and for a moment I thought he was going to walk over towards him.

'Quiet as you can, sir,' I whispered, holding a finger to my lips.

'What's that?' demanded the captain, attempting to whisper back but not making a terribly good job of it.

'There's an ants' nest just beside the rabbit hole,' I said. 'They're quiet at the moment but if they get disturbed they could be deadly. We think they're fighting ants.'

The captain stepped back a pace.

'We need to keep away,' I whispered. 'If we make too much noise, or if the ants hear us walking near their nest they could panic.'

'I say,' said the captain. 'Is that chap OK?'

'He'll be fine,' I said. 'He's an expert on ants. But he told me not to let anyone get too close while he's getting his ball out.'

'Damned brave fellow,' said the captain, lowering his head but not his voice. He backed away a little further. 'I'd have just played a fresh ball,' he said.

'Alfred hates waste,' I said. 'He needs every penny he can. He uses 50% of his earnings to sponsor an orphanage in Thailand.'

'Good God!' said the captain. He coughed nervously. 'Give him my congratulations. Er, hope he finds his ball.'

'Thank you,' I whispered.

And with that the captain turned and walked away.

Sweating profusely I collapsed onto the grass, lowered my head and murmured a quiet prayer of thanks.

* * *

'Did it go OK?' asked Rupert, a few minutes later, as I pushed Alfred, now strapped back onto the trolley, up onto the green. I was once more wearing his woolly hat.

'It went fine,' I told him.

'You look pale,' said Humphrey. 'Are you OK?'

'Would you like to sell me a life insurance policy?' I asked him.

'Not just at the moment,' said Humphrey. 'Not the way you look. Not without a full medical.'

Nigel chipped up onto the green. Rupert, whose ball was already on the green, looked over towards me. 'Alfred is in the bunker isn't he?'

I agreed that Alfred's ball was, indeed, in the bunker.

'Play it out then, old chap,' he said.

I played Alfred's ball out of the bunker. To my delight it landed around six feet from the hole. The rest finished their putts. I just missed the six footer.

'Five for me,' said Rupert. 'How many did Alfred take?'

'Three,' I told him.

'Three?' exclaimed Rupert.

'Three,' I said firmly. 'It would have been a two if he hadn't missed that putt.'

I got some funny looks but Rupert wrote Alfred down for a three.

* * *

On the 18th Alfred played brilliantly. He finished the hole with a magnificent long iron and a long putt and scored his fifth three of the final nine. He collapsed as the five of us left the green, and died seconds after he had signed Rupert's card.

The doctor, who had been called out of the bar, was surprised at the speed with which rigor mortis set in. Rupert explained that the weather was probably responsible and Humphrey added that Alfred had been complaining of stiffness all afternoon so the doctor, who had had a few whiskies and wasn't thinking too straight, said it could well be a mixture of the two.

When the scores were added up Alfred turned out to be the winner of the Captain's Cup. It was quite a surprise to everyone because Alfred had always been a rather mediocre player and had never before looked like winning any tournament, let alone anything as prestigious as the Captain's Cup. 'It was, reported the local paper the following week, 'Alfred's sparkling form on the homeward half of the course which led directly to his victory.'

Alfred's widow was so delighted at her late husband's belated golfing success that she sent a cheque for £500 to the bar so that we could all celebrate Alfred's hole in one and his victory.

Alfred was more popular dead than he had ever been alive.

Chapter Twelve

'Golf Is A Four Letter Word.'

Simon's approach shot on the 18th had hit the upslope of a small hummock on the left edge of the course and flown right over the bunker into which it would have otherwise have surely landed.

'Lucky bounce!' cried Oliver as we all met on the green.

'Nonsense,' said Simon. 'I was just using the natural contours of the golf course. It's an essential part of course management. All the top professionals do it.' He paused. 'Naturally,' he added, 'they're not always as successful as that.' He paused and gazed longingly at his ball. 'I could have been a contender,' he told us.

'Every golfer believes that,' Oliver told me. 'Every golfer I have ever met has harboured the same mistaken self-belief. It is what keeps most of them going as they hack their way around the course.' His ball was furthest from the hole. He crouched over it and tried to read the line to the hole.

'Don't you ever think that?' I asked him when he'd hit his ball. It rolled eight or nine feet past the hole.

'Of course,' said Oliver, shaking his head. 'But in my case it happens to be true. I just need to be a little more consistent.'

'Pshaw!' said Simon, derisively. 'Consistency is vastly overrated.' From about twenty feet away from the hole he curled a putt to within a yard. He smiled.

'No, it's not. I need some consistency,' said Oliver. 'Remember that drive of mine at the fourth last month? Wonderful. Straight as an arrow. And that putt two months ago to win the 17th? It must have been 40 feet if it was an inch. It curled right for ten feet, went straight, swung left and then curled right before dropping into the centre of the hole. No one could have played that shot better. The average professional would have been happy to have left his ball within two or three feet of the hole. If I could play my best shots all the time I'd be a brilliant player.'

Gerald who hadn't said a word tapped in a ten foot putt for an excellent bogey – his best hole of the round. He danced a small jig of delight and kissed his putter.

'You don't need consistency,' Simon told Oliver. 'You've got plenty of consistency. In fact you've got far too much consistency. You are awash with consistency. Your best shots are a result of inconsistency.'

Oliver looked at him, clearly puzzled. It was my turn to putt. I left my ball hanging on the lip of the hole. Well, it was no more than a foot away at the most.

'How many good shots do you play in a round?' Simon asked Oliver.

Oliver thought for a moment or two. 'Two or three,' he confessed. 'Sometimes less. Sometimes a few more.'

'And how many bad shots?'

'All the rest, I suppose,' admitted Oliver.

There was silence then for a while as we all holed out. I took one more putt, Oliver took two and Simon needed three. It had been a pretty average round for all of us but there had, as always, been moments of glory to remember.

'It's consistency that gives you all your bad shots,' explained Simon as we walked off the green. He put his arm around Oliver's shoulders. 'I don't wish to be rude but you're consistently bad. You're bad at golf because you are consistent.'

Oliver, who was beginning to see the point of Simon's argument, looked miserable.

'The good shots come rarely because they come when you aren't being consistent,' explained Simon. 'The problem is that you don't know what it is that you've changed – or in what way you've been inconsistent – when you play a good shot.'

'Dammit, you're right,' agreed Oliver, hanging his head and looking even more miserable. 'So what do I do?'

'I've no idea,' said Simon.

'Oh come on,' said Oliver. 'You can't stop there!'

We headed for the clubhouse. Gerald leading, me following and Simon and Oliver walking together. 'When you play a shot you won't know whether it will be any good or not until you've played it,' said Simon. 'And by the time you've played it, it's too late to spot whether you're being consistent or inconsistent.'

'You're a great help,' said Oliver.

'Well there is one thing you can do,' suggested Simon.

'What's that?'

'Play as inconsistently as you possibly can,' said Simon. 'The most consistent player I ever knew was also the worst I've ever seen.'

I turned round. 'Worse than me?' I asked hopefully.

'How the hell do I deliberately play inconsistently?' asked Oliver.

'Worse even than you, Tom,' said Simon. 'Although he had been playing golf for nearly twenty years Wilfred was probably the worst player in the club. I always marvelled that he could afford to buy the number of balls he lost. I'll tell you about him when we get into the bar.'

'I suppose I could just try changing my grip and my stance for every shot,' muttered Oliver to himself. 'But I'd have to try and remember how I'd played the shot so that I'd know whether or not what I was doing was working.' He brightened up. 'I can do that,' he said to himself.

* * *

As we sat around the fire sipping our first drinks of the afternoon, Simon proceeded to tell me the story of Wilfred, the most consistent player he had ever known and whose very consistency proved quite conclusively that consistency has nothing whatsoever to do with quality.

Wilfred's main problem, said Simon, was that he had a slice.

'It wasn't just an ordinary slice, the sort that comes and goes. And it wasn't one of those slices that results in the ball veering ever so slightly into the rough. Wilfred's slice was permanent and unvarying. If golf is a game where consistency counts then Wilfred should have been a winner of numerous major championships.

He was the most consistent player I ever saw. His slice always resulted in the ball ending up almost at right angles to the spot where it should have been.'

'I remember seeing him,' said Gerald, nodding. 'This is all quite true.'

'Wilfred's slice inevitably led to some strange occurrences,' said Simon. 'Once, for example, I saw him slice a ball through the open window of a passing train. The railway line was normally regarded as safe from such attacks but Wilfred somehow managed to get his ball into the train. I remember him watching the train disappear into the distance with a very sad look on his face.'

'It was a new ball,' he said. 'You'd have thought that someone might have thrown the ball out again.' I found out later that he had telephoned the railway company, identified the train as the 11.07 from Paddington and asked the Lost Property Office if anyone had reported finding a ball on the train. Sadly, no one had.'

'Rather reckless to identify himself as the owner of the ball,' I said. 'It might, after all, have landed in someone's dinner or damaged an expensive hat.'

'Oh people didn't think like that in those days,' said Gerald. 'If someone tripped over a loose bit of paving stone they'd just get up, brush themselves down, curse a bit and carry on. These days people rush off to see a solicitor before they even brush themselves down.'

'Go on about Wilfred,' said Oliver. 'I never saw him play.'

'Well eventually,' continued Simon, 'after umpteen lessons and after buying every book he could find on the subject Wilfred decided that life had given him a slice and that he would just have to learn to live with it. He became quite philosophical about it.'

'Sensible chap,' said Oliver nodding.

'Exactly,' said Simon. 'The one good thing about his slice was that it was consistent and it was this very consistency that enabled him to find a way to deal with the problem. He would stand on the tee and prepare to drive looking for all the world as though he was going to hit the ball at right angles to the direction of the green. While the rest of us were standing looking down the fairway over our left shoulders – or right shoulders in the case of left-handers –

he would be standing in such a way that he only had to lift his head to look straight down the fairway.'

'When he hit the ball it would fly off over whatever rough or trees there were on the left hand side of the tee and suddenly veer to the right and come back round onto the centre of the fairway,' continued Simon. 'After a while he got very good at this and could send his ball straight down the fairway with remarkable consistency.'

'Of course,' said Simon, 'on some holes there were insurmountable problems and he simply couldn't start the ball off in his eccentric direction because of large trees or houses standing in the way. When that was the case he would use a seven iron and chip off the tee until he was in a position where he could use a long iron (which he also sliced) and get some distance down the fairway with that.'

'It must have been extraordinary to watch,' said Oliver.

'Oh it was,' said Gerald. 'People used to sit out on the terrace when he was playing. We had a fixed telescope in those days and one chap would look through it and give us a running commentary on what was happening.'

Simon said that it was fascinating to watch Wilfred get round a course this way and that it was particularly good fun to go out for a round with people who'd never seen him play before.

'They used to watch with astonishment as he drove off the side of the first tee and curved his ball back round into position in the middle of the short grass,' said Simon. 'Once, a member of the club committee came to watch because he thought it might be against the rules but as luck would have it everything Wilfred hit that day went perfectly straight and he had to give up before he left the first tee because he ran out of balls. It was the first time it had ever happened to him and he was terribly upset.'

'You played with him?' asked Gerald.

'Oh yes, quite a few times,' said Simon. I was a young lad and I'd play with anyone in those days. I remember very vividly one game the two of us played. We both nearly got arrested because of Wilfred's damned slice.'

* * *

The real problems started, said Simon, on one of the holes

which run alongside the road. He couldn't remember which one it was.

'For some reason or other Wilfred's ball didn't curve back that day. It just flew straight over the hedge and landed on the road. Fortunately, there wasn't any traffic about. We both saw it quite clearly bouncing on the roadway. But the camber of the road threw it to the left and neither of us was absolutely sure just where it had ended up. Wilfred claimed that he'd seen it running along the gutter and, gloomy as ever, suggested that it had probably fallen down a drain. There was a row of houses and little shops running on the other side of the road in those days and I insisted that the ball had bounced onto the pavement and was almost certainly lying in a shop doorway, sitting up on an old-fashioned, bristly door mat. I was just saying this to cheer him up – he was a pretty gloomy sort of fellow. To be honest I didn't have the faintest idea where it had gone. Anyway, I left my bag on the fairway and the two of us climbed through a gap in the hedge. Wilfred took his bag with him in case he could find his ball and play it back onto the fairway. He was used to playing out of all sorts of strange places.'

'Eventually,' said Simon, 'Wilfred came across his ball more or less by accident. It wasn't on the pavement or in the gutter. It had bounced straight through a shoe shop window and had ended up in the middle of a carefully constructed window display. Looking quite out of place it lay there nestling between a pair of patent leather dancing pumps and a pair of farmer's Wellington boots. The streets used to be full of shoe shops in those days.'

'Most of the broken glass had fallen inwards and was strewn around in dangerous looking shards. 'Do you think bits of broken window pane count as moveable or immovable hazards?' asked Wilfred. 'The bits on the floor are no problem, but what about the bits hanging loose in the window frame? Are they like bits of bendy twig that I can't remove. Or are they like bits of debris that can be moved out of the way without any penalty?"

'Wilfred looked distressed by this dilemma,' said Simon. 'He pursed his lips and started leafing through his pocket Rules of Golf. It was getting rather worn and several pages were already coming loose.'

"If I can't move them,' Wilfred went on, 'I can't get in to play the ball because the hole isn't big enough as it is and the door is locked because the shop is shut."

"Well the glass is man-made,' I reasoned. 'So it's an obstruction and I suppose you're entitled to move as much as you like."

'Wilfred seemed satisfied with that and he used his one iron (a club we all carried but none of us ever used) to knock out enough glass to make a hole big enough for him to climb through. When he'd done that he pulled on his golf glove, bent down and clambered into the shop window.'

'When I realised what he was planning to do I was absolutely horrified,' said Simon. 'You can't play out of there!' I told him. 'Not out of a shop window!'

"Course I can!' insisted Wilfred cheerily. 'If I cock my wrists a bit and just play a little chip shot I should get out with no problems at all."

'It was only then, while he was settling into his stance and I was trying to keep as quiet as I could, that I heard the burglar alarm ringing,' said Simon. 'The two of us stood, frozen with fear, listening to the insistent clatter of this damned burglar alarm bell. I said I thought we would be surrounded by the police within seconds and that we'd end up disgraced, broken men. I said we'd be lucky if we got away with thirty years hard labour. Wilfred said he thought that I was probably exaggerating a little. He said that he had plenty of time to play his shot and that he would leave a £5 note behind to pay for all the damage. He said that no one ever took any notice of burglar alarms and that the police were only ever called when people got fed up of the noise and wanted the alarm switched off.'

'While I hopped from one foot to the other and peered up and down the street looking for police cars Wilfred calmly moved the loose shards of glass from around his ball and took a couple of practice swings. Then he chipped his ball out of the shop window and back onto the pavement. It was a splendid shot. Indeed, it was probably one of the best recovery shots I've ever seen played by an amateur. It was certainly the very best shot I've ever seen anyone play from a shop window. The only snag was that in his enthusiasm to ensure that he didn't leave the ball where it was, Wilfred continued with a full follow-through and there wasn't room for him to complete his swing without sending his club crashing into the remains of the shop window. The result was that another few yards of plate glass came crashing down around our feet. Some of the glass stayed in the shop window but most of it fell onto the pavement. We were up to our ankles in broken glass.'

Simon leant forward. 'Now I don't know whether you've ever noticed this,' he said, 'but broken glass is a bit like blood in that a relatively small amount of it will go an awfully long way and make a tremendous amount of mess. Cut yourself shaving and you may think that you've only lost a few drops of blood but I can pretty well guarantee that within seconds there will be blood everywhere. Those few drops will have stained your shirt, your jacket, your trousers, your shoes, your hat and your overcoat on the other side of the room. There will be blood on the carpet, on the curtains, on the potted plant on your window sill and on the ceiling. Even your wallet, tucked inside your jacket pocket, will have blood smeared all over it when you pull it out. Well, it's much the same with glass. It seems to have similar qualities to blood in that an apparently small amount of it can spread over quite a huge area. Drop a small drinking glass on the kitchen floor and within seconds there will be bits of glass all around your house. There will be bits of glass down the back of the sofa, in the breast pocket of your dinner jacket upstairs in the bedroom, in behind the books in your study, in the piano and even up in your loft. There will be bits of glass hiding in the garden that won't turn up for months. A small drinking glass that can't possibly weigh more than an ounce or two will shatter into several hundred weight of glass fragments.'

'So you can imagine what happens when a whole shop window shatters. There were bits of broken glass spread all over the pavement and all across the road. There were bits of broken glass in my pockets and in my shoes. There were slivers of glass in the gutter, in shop doorways up and down the street and scattered across the roof of a car parked nearby. There was so much glass that if you'd glued all those bits of broken glass back together they would have probably made a window a mile square.'

'Wilfred seemed unperturbed by it all. He stepped out of the window and watched his ball bouncing along the road. He watched it narrowly miss a car parked on the opposite side of the street. He watched it bounce off a lamp-post and across the pavement on the other side of the road. And he watched it smash through the large plate glass window of another shoe shop no more than fifty yards away.'

'Oh no' groaned Oliver. 'I don't believe this.'

'It's true,' insisted Simon. 'Wilfred wanted to carry on and play out of this shop window too. He said he thought he'd got the hang of it now and the trick was to play a gentle chip and run shot rather than a full-blooded blow. He said he thought he could chip his ball out through the hole it had made.'

'But I said (or rather shouted, for there were now two alarm bells ringing and both were making an awful din) that if he insisted on playing out of a second shop window I was leaving him there and that as far as I was concerned the hole and the match were mine. I also said I would never play golf with him again. Well, that pretty well made up his mind for him because he had a lot of difficulty finding partners and I was one of the few people who would play with him.'

'So Wilfred dropped another ball, lost a stroke and played it. That one bounced off a car and went down a side street. We got quite lost for a while after that. I remember it took us some time to find out way back to the golf course. Wilfred was the only person I ever played with who knew where his ball was but lost the course.'

'When Wilfred finally holed out he reckoned he'd taken 386 for the hole. I privately thought it was 387 but I didn't like to argue too much so I let it stand.'

'So there you are,' concluded Simon. 'Next time you pray for a little more consistency in your game just remember Wilfred and be grateful that unlike him you don't usually know where your next ball is likely to go.'

We all agreed that Wilfred's story was a salutary one.

'I think Simon's really hit on something terrific,' said Oliver. 'I'm going to try being as inconsistent as possible from now on.'

* * *

Two days later, when we next went round together, Oliver

showed just how inconsistent he could be. He sprayed balls in every direction and went round in 146.

'Your idea doesn't work,' he told Simon in the lounge afterwards.

'But you were still being consistent,' Simon insisted.

'No I wasn't! Every time I hit the ball I changed my grip, my stance, my swing, my follow-through. I changed everything. There was no consistency at all in my game.'

'Yes, there was,' said Simon. 'You were very consistent. You were consistently inconsistent. And you were consistently awful.'

Oliver looked at him. 'I think your theory stinks,' he said.

Chapter Thirteen

'Too Many Clubs And Not Enough Balls.'

It is a common assumption among golfers (particularly ones who are not very good at the game) that the more clubs a golfer has in his bag, and the more he has paid for them, the better he will play. This is, I had discovered, pretty much a lie.

When golf professionals sell matched sets of irons they advise that the five iron will hit the ball so far, the seven iron will hit it not quite so far and the six iron will hit it somewhere between the two. This, of course, turned out to be nonsense. Sometimes I would hit a seven iron two yards. On other occasions I would hit it 150 yards. I could, in truth, have managed with, perhaps, four clubs: something with which to hit the ball from the tee, an iron for hitting it off grass, a wedgy one for hitting the ball out of bunkers and the rough and a putter. If this secret truth (along the lines of the tale of the Emperor's New Clothes) ever becomes common knowledge among club golfers then the golf club industry will collapse and will have to encourage the game's rule makers to introduce a rule defining the minimum number of clubs a player must carry in his bag.

* * *

At the end of one Sunday morning round, as we struggled out of our soaked clothes (the new waterproof jacket and trousers I had purchased would, so the salesman assured me, withstand water fired from a high pressure fireman's hose but the storms and winds which battered our course had proved too much for them) Simon, naked except for a pair of boxer shorts which appeared to have been made from an old Union Jack flag, rubbed at his shoulder and groaned. 'I hate it when trolleys are banned,' he complained. 'Dragging that bag around the course doesn't do my poor old joints any good at all.'

'I don't know how you lift your bag,' said Oliver. 'What on earth have you got in it?'

'Just the usual stuff,' said Simon, rather defensively. 'Fourteen clubs, a few balls, couple of gloves, tees...'

'It weighs a ton,' said Gerald, picking up Simon's bag. 'Are you sure you haven't got half a dozen gold bars stuffed in the base?'

'It's just the usual bits and pieces,' protested Simon. 'I bet your bag weighs as much.' He stood up gingerly and tip-toed across to where Gerald's bag was leaning against a bench. He lifted the bag by the handle at the top. 'Yours is heavier than mine,' he said. 'How the hell do you carry that thing round with you?'

'Empty out your bags,' said Oliver, who frequently plays with a small bag and a selection of no more than eight or nine clubs. 'Let's have a look at what you've got in them.'

Simon pulled down the zip on the main pocket of his bag and emptied the contents onto a bench. When he'd finished with the main pocket he emptied the smaller pockets. He even removed all the clubs. We all stood around and stared at the mountain of rubbish which he had excavated from the depths. Here is what we saw:

2 drivers

1x3 wood

1x5 wood

1x7 wood

Irons numbered 3,4,5,6,7,8,9,

3 wedges

1 sand iron

1 putter

2 brand new boxes of golf balls (half a dozen balls in each box)

9 loose golf balls in good, playable condition

7 loose golf balls so badly cut as to be unusable even on the practice ground

28 assorted golf tees

2 sodden golf gloves

2 brand new golf gloves still in their packets

1 golf glove that had perished and gone slightly mouldy

1 mobile telephone which Simon could not remember ever owning, let alone losing

1 long out-of-date chocolate bar which had melted at least once and then reset in a different shape

2 packets of biscuits (with the expiry date on both two years past)

1 half empty bottle of cola

1 empty lager tin

1 spare sweater

1 small handtowel

1 large towel which belonged to a London hotel

1 paperback summary of the golf rules

1 hardback book packed with advice on how to get out of bunkers

1 patented and unused device for keeping score

1 ball cleaner

1 Swiss Army penknife

1 wooden stake

A variety of old sweet packets, crisp packets, ball wrappers, empty glove packets and old score cards. And, right at the bottom of the main pocket a disgusting, smelly mess which had clearly once been a banana but which now appeared to be home to a nation of assorted bacteria.

'What on earth is the wooden stake for?' I asked.

'Vampires,' said Simon quickly. 'There used to be a lot of them on this course.' He paused. 'But there aren't now.' He laughed. No one else did. The joke was too old even for us to laugh at it.

'Balls which land close to staked trees have to be moved to within two club lengths,' explained Gerald. 'So carrying your own stake with you can be quite useful.'

'I once played with an administrator from Hartlepool who tried to convince me that a 150 foot tall oak was still staked,' said Oliver. 'The tree that had been tied to the stake had died and been broken off, leaving just the stake remaining. It was forty feet away from the oak but the chap from Hartlepool insisted that the three foot high stake was supporting it.'

'What happened?' I asked.

'In the end I was so impressed by his chutzpa that I let him get away with it,' said Oliver with a shrug.

'I once knew a chap who carried a Ground Under Repair notice in his bag,' said Simon. 'He used to just stick it into the ground if he didn't like his lie. But I thought that was cheating.'

'Because you didn't have one?' asked Oliver, smiling.

'Actually, I did try to get one,' confessed Simon. 'But the groundsman hammers them in very well here. I tried to buy a spare one from him but he wanted an outrageous price.'

'How much?'

'Thirty quid.'

'Worth it.'

'Maybe. I'll perhaps have another word with him. See if I can get him down to twenty.'

'Isn't that the knife I gave you?' asked Gerald, reaching for the penknife. 'If you don't want it I'll have it back. Nice looking knife.'

'You've never given me anything!' retorted Simon, smacking Gerald's wrist, as a teacher will smack an errant pupil. 'Leave it alone. I like that knife.'

'I gave you flu once,' responded Gerald, pulling his hand out of range and rubbing his wrist.

'Only because you'd finished with it,' said Simon. 'A second-hand disease doesn't count as a present, does it?' He looked at me as he added the final two words.

I shook my head.

'You've got some of those funny sized balls there,' said Oliver. He picked up a ball from Simon's bag which had rolled along the floor and rested against his left foot.

'I like the bigger ball,' said Simon.

'I don't think they're legal,' said Gerald, who knows a good deal about these things though what he knows isn't always accurate or reliable. He and Oliver then had a spirited conversation about the relative advantages and disadvantages of small balls and large balls. They talked wisely about flight, spin and distance and about the need to prevent modern golfers, armed with wonderful new technology, from turning par 5 holes into par 4 holes and par 4 holes into pitch and putt holes.

'I definitely prefer the bigger ball,' insisted Simon.

'Why?' asked Oliver.

'The bigger ball is easier to find in the rough.'

Oliver and Gerald looked at one another but for a moment neither of them spoke.

'I hadn't thought of that,' admitted Gerald. 'Can't argue with you.'

'Pretty convincing,' agreed Oliver.

'You certainly carry a lot of balls with you,' said Gerald, staring at the balls which had been emptied out of Simon's bag.

'Not enough,' said Simon. 'I never seem to have enough balls.'

'I know what you mean,' said Oliver. 'Too many clubs and not enough balls. That's always my problem.'

'It's your turn,' said Simon, looking at Gerald. He scooped up some of the rubbish he had taken out of his bag and carried it across to a litter bin. He used the small towel (which was filthy dirty) to scoop up the decaying banana and threw the whole sorry mess into the same bin.

'Have you ever counted the number of clubs in your bag?' Oliver asked Simon. Simon ignored him.

Gerald's bag was even more tightly crammed than Simon's. When he had finished emptying his bag we saw that it had contained:

3 drivers

Irons numbered 3,4,5,6,7,8,9

3 wedges

3 putters

19 loose balls in good, playable condition

4 and a half balls which were unplayable

3 golf tees (since Gerald invariably borrows tees from other people this was more than we had expected him to find)

1 plaid shirt which Gerald denied he had ever seen before

1 lady's upper body undergarment in black lace, with a broken strap (ditto)

1 spare pair of waterproof trousers with a large tear in the rear

1 short-sleeved sweater

1 long-sleeved sweater which had been placed in the bag wet and which was now covered in mildew

1 former apple

1 tin of boiled sweets, all of which had stuck together to form a huge impenetrable and unbreakable mass

1 folding umbrella

1 red sock

4 pens (none of which worked)

1 propelling pencil, with no leads

1 roll of 35 mm camera film which had been exposed but not processed (Gerald had no idea how old the film was nor what photographs it contained)

1 small trophy marked 'Champion 1972' (Gerald could not remember what the trophy related to but none of us – not even him – thought it had anything to do with golf)

1 penknife, opened so that the device designed for removing stones from horses' hooves was visible

1 hardback copy of a book which promised to help the reader lower his handicap by 10 strokes in as many weeks

1 golf magazine with the cover torn off

1 paperback copy of a golf novel by P.G.Wodehouse

1 gadget for cleaning the grooves on golf clubs and the dimples on golf balls

3 special tripod tees for use on hard frozen ground

1 laser range finder

3 golf balls in a packet which promised that the contents would glow and enable the user to play in the dark without difficulty

1 street map of Wolverhampton (a place which Gerald claimed he could not remember ever visiting)

1 plastic yo-yo

1 packet of spare spikes for a pair of golf shoes which Gerald

had thrown away three years earlier

1 small radio which Gerald said he had taken out on the course with him during the final day of a golf tournament which Jack Nicklaus had won. The radio didn't work and when Gerald prised open the back with a pitch repairer we could see that the batteries which powered it were several years past their best and were now covered in an unpleasant looking layer of something pungent in off-white. Holding it carefully between forefinger and thumb Gerald carried the radio to the nearest bin and dropped it in.

'You've got more than 14 clubs there,' said Oliver. 'And Simon has 17.'

'Possibly,' agreed Gerald. 'But I always count them before I start a round.'

We all looked at him.

'Nearly always.'

No one said anything.

'Often.'

Still no one said anything.

'Sometimes I forget,' he admitted. 'But I can't decide which putter to use. And anyway, I think that having a limit of 14 is distinctly unreasonable. Who decided on 14? Why not 16? Or 40? The fact is that on any one day there will always be one club in my bag which has broken. It will be impossible to see anything wrong with the club, but it won't work properly. Temporary metal fatigue is the best explanation I can think of – a sort of stress-related disorder for golf clubs. So I need something to replace it.'

'Does it make a difference to your score if you have more clubs in your bag?' asked Simon.

'Not really,' admitted Gerald. 'In fact,' he admitted, 'if I've got too much stuff with me I sometimes get confused and can't decide which club to use.'

'Some of this stuff would be worth a fortune to a collector,' said Oliver.

We all looked at him.

'People buy old golfing memorabilia,' he explained. 'If stuff is old enough it can become quite valuable.'

'You'll be a collector's item yourself then soon,' said Gerald. He started to pull together the things he'd emptied out of his bag. 'Leave my stuff alone.'

'This putter has got a wooden shaft!' exclaimed Oliver.

'Hickory,' said Gerald. 'It's a Brandon Mills putter.'

'You're playing with clubs which should be in a museum!' said Oliver.

Simon took Gerald's bag from him and lifted it up. 'Your bag weighs a ton even when it's empty!' he said.

'It's real leather,' explained Gerald. 'It's not one of those horrible plastic things you chaps use.'

'You need new grips on your irons,' said Oliver. 'There's mould on this one.'

'I don't use that one very often,' said Gerald. He grabbed his clubs and thrust them back into his bag.

Oliver's bag, a comparatively flimsy affair which he used when trolleys were not allowed on the course, was fitted with just one pocket. This contained four spare balls, a neat plastic box containing tees, a pencil stub, a half used golf glove, a ball marker, a pitch repairer and a packet of indigestion tablets.

'But what do you carry in your big bag?' demanded Simon.

With some embarrassment, Oliver opened the door to his locker. 'Some of this stuff,' he said, removing a patented wrist brace, a plastic and leather foot wedge which fitted into the back of his shoe to stop his left heel lifting off the ground, a thing which looked rather like a strait-jacket which Oliver explained was designed to help him keep his upper arms together and a patented club which, the manufacturers apparently claimed, would automatically correct a player's hook or slice and make the ball go straight.

'I want one of those!' said Gerald.

'Does it work?' asked Simon.

Oliver looked at them pityingly and held the club out. 'Who wants it?' he asked. 'It cost me £399. You can have it for a fiver.'

Simon and Gerald both shook their heads. Oliver tossed the club back into his locker.

'What's this?' asked Simon, picking up a large, sealed envelope which had fallen out of Oliver's locker.

Oliver picked it up, examined it briefly and smiled with affection. 'I sent away to Japan for this,' he told us. 'The advertisement described it as "the single most sensational secret in the history of golf."' He turned the envelope over and read from it : 'Be to learn the simpler, magical move which to solve all your golfer problems and guarantee permanent greatest golf.'

'What is it?' demanded Gerald. 'What's the secret?'

'I haven't opened it,' said Oliver, holding up the envelope so that we could all see that it was still sealed.

'Why?' asked Simon. 'Why on earth haven't you opened it?'

'To begin with I didn't open it because it felt that it might be cheating,' he said quietly. 'Taking advantage of some trick that no one else knew. Then, as the days went by and turned into weeks, I decided that I would keep the envelope so that if things got really bad out on the course I would know that I had something to fall back on. A secret solution that would help me out of a hole – or, more precisely, into one.'

'But your game is always awful!' said Simon.

'I know,' agreed Oliver. 'But I've had the envelope so long that now I daren't open it. I've got so much faith in the contents that I'm terrified that if I open the envelope I'll be disappointed. And then I won't have the comfort of knowing that I've got the envelope to open.'

'How much did you pay for this mysterious secret?' asked Simon.

'Seventy nine dollars,' replied Oliver without hesitation. 'And I had to pay the bank £20 so that I could send a bank draft in dollars.'

'Open it,' said Gerald. 'I want to know what it says.'

'Put it back in the locker,' said Simon quietly. 'I don't think I could cope with opening it either.'

Gerald stared at him, stared at me and then stared at Oliver. He threw up his arms. 'Put the bloody thing back in the locker,' he agreed.

My bag, still relatively new, was almost embarrassingly free of clutter and contained only the essentials.

'No wonder my bag was so heavy,' complained Simon, staring at the mound of material he had taken from his bag. Looking at the pile it was difficult to see how he'd managed to get it all in there. He picked up another handful of debris, carried it over to a waste bin and tossed it in. He crammed some of the balls, one of the spare gloves and one of the towels into his locker. 'I suppose I ought to clean this bag out sometime,' he said. He sniffed the larger pocket, where the banana had rotted, and, recoiling in horror, zipped it up again. 'But not just now,' he said. 'I'll do it some other time.' He stuffed the remaining balls, the two new gloves and the remaining towel into smaller pockets and then reached for his dry shirt and started getting dressed.

Gerald threw away the stuff he didn't need, didn't want or didn't know the owner of and then tossed the remains back into his bag.

When he had restocked his bag he lifted it. 'It's no lighter!' he exclaimed, astonished. 'Feel it!'

I lifted his bag. It was still extremely heavy.

'It's all the clubs,' said Simon, lifting his own bag.

'I really don't need this many clubs,' said Gerald. He rifled through the clubs in his bag. 'I never use this, or this, or that, or this.' He pulled four clubs out of his bag and put them into his locker.

'I hate this club,' said Simon, pulling out a two iron. 'And this one.' He pulled out a three iron. 'And I never use this,' he said, extracting a sand wedge which was covered with a thin layer of rust. He finished buttoning his shirt and took his trousers out of his locker.

'I reckon we could play just as well with a quarter of the clubs,' said Oliver.

'Well, I'm down to fourteen,' said Simon, pulling on his trousers. 'A quarter of fourteen is three and a half. So which club shall I cut in two?'

'Just three clubs then,' said Oliver. 'I bet we could play just as well as we did today if we all played with just three clubs each.'

'Don't be daft,' said Gerald. 'Why would everyone struggle round the course with fourteen clubs if they could make do with three?'

'I didn't say everyone could make do with three,' said Oliver. 'The professionals probably need fourteen. And the club manufacturers and osteopaths would like us all to carry fourteen. But at our level I reckon we'd probably do just as well carrying three clubs.'

'I'd feel a bit of a prat going round with just three clubs in a bag,' said Simon, who was now putting on his socks.

'When the game started they only played with one club,' Gerald pointed out. 'It was a Scottish shepherd who started it all off,' he said. 'I read about it in a book my ex-mother-in-law gave me for my birthday last week.'

There was a small silence and then we all apologised for having forgotten Gerald's birthday. Oliver, Gerald and I started dressing too.

Then Oliver, who has a stubborn streak of curiosity running right through the middle of him, like lettering in Blackpool rock, asked Gerald to tell us more about the shepherd.

Gerald responded eagerly. He said that according to the book he'd read the chap who'd invented the game was a shepherd called McGoughlin who lived in Sutherland, right up in the Scottish highlands, and who looked after a huge flock of sheep owned by a laird with the only bit of Scotland not over-run by deer or grouse.

While the other shepherds sat around on the hillsides watching the clouds wandering by, staring at the gorse and heather sprouting and making embroidered smocks to sell to the tourists McGoughlin invented golf. Or so said Gerald.

Simon and Oliver looked impressed. I still wasn't entirely sure that Gerald wasn't making it all up.

'He had one of those big shepherd crooks,' said Gerald. 'The ones that are used for grabbing sheep by the neck, and he turned it upside down and used it for knocking little pebbles around. He started making softer balls out of bits of sheep's gut and eagle feathers when he kept breaking his crooks on the pebbles.'

Gerald went on to explain that to start with McGoughlin used to smash balls around willy nilly, much in the same undirected way that children will kick a stone along the road. But then, said Gerald, he got fed up with this and decided to see if he could make it from one point to another in a limited number of shots. So that he would have precise points to aim at he built small piles of stones on every hilltop and simply knocked his ball of sheep's gut and eagle feathers from one to another. He couldn't count, of course, being illiterate, but he used to pick up a thistle head every time he had a shot and put it into the big pocket at the front of his smock.

'So why is it called 'golf'?' asked Oliver.

'From his name,' explained Gerald. 'When the other shepherds saw him playing they'd say 'There goes old McGoughlin'. And they'd shake their heads at the wonder of it all. Then gradually they started to call what he was doing 'McGoughlin' and finally, when the game came south over the border, the Mc was dropped and the game was known as Goughlin. From that it was only a short step to the name game has today.'

'I never knew that,' said Simon, clearly impressed.

'The point of all this,' said Gerald 'is that when the game started players didn't have bags full of equipment and they didn't even play over formal courses. Old McGoughlin just hammered his ball with his trusty crook and wandered from one hillside to the next. He didn't walk around with a bag of crooks of different shapes and sizes and he didn't have crook covers or grip rougheners either.' He pulled on a shoe and carefully tied the lace. 'That's how we ought to play golf,' he said.

'It does sound more natural,' agreed Simon.

'So why don't we try it?' asked Gerald. 'We wouldn't have to worry about dragging huge bags full of equipment with us or about whether to use a full-blooded four iron or to hold back slightly with a three iron.'

'What exactly did you have in mind?' Simon asked Gerald.

'Well, we could try what Oliver suggested and just use three clubs,' suggested Gerald.

'We'd all feel a lot better at the end of the round,' said Oliver.

'The golf supermarket sells skimpy little bags,' said Gerald. 'I think they're for beginners, boys and old ladies.'

'Get us one each,' said Oliver. He reached into his jacket pocket and took out his wallet. 'How much are they?'

'Dunno,' said Gerald. 'Settle up with me when I've got them. Any particular colour?'

'Just four different colours,' said Oliver. 'It'll save mix-ups.'

'When are we going to conduct this experiment?' asked Simon.

'One Sunday soon?' suggested Oliver. 'We need to give Gerald time to get the bags and all of us time to decide which three clubs we want to use.'

And so it was agreed that one Sunday, before too long, we would conduct an experiment to find out whether or not we really needed to carry so many clubs.

'Keep your score cards from today,' said Oliver. 'And then we can compare how we did.'

Just then the club secretary poked his head around the door. 'Is Tom in here?' he asked. He looked around but did not see me.

'What's up?' asked Gerald. 'Failed to bow properly to the lady captain? Parked his car in the president's space?'

'No, nothing like that,' said the Secretary. 'I need a plumber. The drain in the ladies' shower is blocked again.'

'Who's in there?' asked Simon.

'Just Deidre,' said the secretary. 'She's standing, fully dressed, on a lavatory seat. When I left the water was about three inches below her feet.'

'Poor Deidre,' said Simon. 'I hope she can swim. Tom isn't here I'm afraid. I think he's away on a course. The EU has banned hot taps and plumbers are all having to be retrained.'

'Banned hot taps?'

'So I hear. A bloke in Frankfurt burnt himself.'

The secretary tutted loudly and disappeared.

'Thanks,' I said, when he'd gone.

'Don't mention it,' said Simon. 'Of course, if the place had been stuffed with naked young women covering their modesty with small bars of soap I'd have told him you were here. And I'd have come along as your assistant.'

* * *

We still haven't got round to playing our game of golf with just three clubs each. We have spoken about it several times, and always with considerable enthusiasm, but somehow we have always found a reason to postpone it.

I think the truth is that we are all a little bit afraid. We are worried about what people might say if they see us setting off with such inadequately stacked golf bags. And we are afraid of what might happen.

If it turns out that we play better with three clubs than with 14 (or 17 or 18) what will we do? Will we really be prepared to turn up for the next monthly medal with just three clubs in our bags?

The professionals use 14 clubs and claim they need them all. If we prove that we play at our best with less than a quarter of the number what will that say about our prowess as golfers?

It would have been an interesting exercise.

But the risks are simply too great. We talk about it with great excitement; but we haven't dared try it. And I don't think we ever will.

Chapter Fourteen

'The Custard Cream Solution.'

After eight months, I had still not become what I, or indeed anyone else, could call a great golfer. I still considered it something of a triumph, something well worth mentioning to anyone I met in the bar at the completion of the round, if I managed to play more than three holes with the same ball.

But things were improving. There had been a time when I would have been surprised if I had managed to play more than two consecutive shots, let alone holes, with the same ball.

In the short period of time I'd been playing I had learned a good deal about the game of golf.

I had learned, for example, that golf ball manufacturers put some chemical into their balls which results in them being attracted by water. Once a ball gets anywhere near a pond, a lake or even a stream it will veer from its previous course and head straight for the water. (It was Oliver who first told me this. He said he didn't have any direct evidence for it but that a friend of his who knew someone who worked in a golf ball factory had assured him that it was true. The friend had also told him that in order to make them look good, and make the rest of us think it's worth persevering, the top tournament professionals are given balls which aren't coated with this secret substance.)

And I was becoming accepted into the social life of the club.

The club, I had discovered, had an extremely complex administrative structure which was, for many members, just as important as the acres of green and pleasant land which stretched away in front of the clubhouse. In addition to a president there were four vice-presidents, 29 life presidents, a captain, a treasurer and a Greens Committee chairman. There were more committees than any normal person could (or would want to) count and every committee had a chairman, a secretary and a treasurer. The club was positively awash with persons of importance.

Fifteen of the life presidents were former presidents, since anyone who was ever made president became a life president at the end of their year in office and were entitled to hear the staff continue to refer to them as Mr President. The club favoured the American style, whereby every former president remains president for life.

The other life presidents had been elected democratically by giving the club fairly indecent amounts of money.

'If you want to pay for the roof to be mended you too can be a life president,' said Gerald one day.

It was, I suppose, inevitable that even I would eventually end up on a committee.

* * *

'I've put you forward for a vacant place on the Catering Committee Sub Committee (Billiards Room),' said the club secretary. 'They've only got 19 people on that committee at the moment. They need another member and your name has come up. Would you be prepared to accept nomination?'

'Is there a rule about that? Do there have to be 20 people on every committee?' I asked.

'Not exactly,' answered the secretary. 'But we like to keep our committees full. It means that everyone in the club can feel that they are part of the decision making process.'

'So all committees have 20 members?'

'Oh yes,' nodded the secretary.

'To keep things streamlined? I suppose more than 20 people on a committee would be pretty cumbersome.'

'Well actually,' admitted the secretary. 'It's because you can only get 20 chairs into the committee room.'

'And you want to know if I would accept if I was nominated?'

'That's it.'

'It's what the Queen does before she sends out invitations to her garden parties, isn't it?'

'What's that?'

'Sends out a preliminary letter to see if you'll accept the invitation.'

'I believe Her Majesty does do something similar,' agreed the secretary.

'And you say that I'm going to be on the Billiards Room Committee?' I asked.

'The Catering Committee Sub Committee (Billiards Room),' said the secretary, carefully correcting me. It's one of our oldest established committees.'

'Does the club have a billiards room?' I asked. I hadn't spotted one. I rather like billiards.

The secretary shook his head. 'I'm afraid not. As far as anyone can remember it disappeared in 1956 when the clubhouse was remodelled to include a ladies' lounge.' He brightened up. 'But I can assure you that the absence of a billiard table is something the members of the Billiards Room Committee feel very strongly about. Their Billiards Room Committee Home Fixtures Sub Committee sends the Club's Management Committee a strongly worded memo about it every autumn.'

'The Billiards Committee has a Home Fixtures Sub Committee?'

'Oh yes.'

'But how can they organise any home fixtures when they don't have a table?'

'They arrange the fixtures and then cancel them all just before they're due to take place,' explained the secretary. 'It's something of a tradition now.'

'Why on earth do they do that?'

'I believe they feel that if they stop arranging fixtures then it will be seen as a de facto admission that the Billiard Club is no longer fully operational,' said the secretary.

'So, what does the Catering Committee Sub Committee (Billiards Room) actually do?' I asked.

'Well, it's in charge of catering for the billiards room and in charge of catering for the committee which is in charge of the billiard room and for the committee which is in charge of setting up fixtures for the billiard room. It is, in fact, in charge of all the catering for anything to do with the billiards room – including, of course, the catering for the Catering Committee Sub Committee (Billiards Room).'

'But the billiards room doesn't exist?'

'Well, as you say, the billiards room doesn't actually exist in that there isn't a physical space dedicated to the accommodation of a billiard table in the old-fashioned material way, but there is a very active Billiards Room Committee.'

'What sort of catering is needed for a billiard room which doesn't exist?'

'Oh you'd be surprised,' said the club secretary.

'I suspect I would be,' I agreed.

'The main responsibility, I suppose, is, er, organising the refreshments for the committees.'

'Do they have meals sent in?'

'Not exactly meals.'

'Biscuits? Tea?'

'Definitely biscuits and definitely tea.'

'Does the committee have to make the tea?'

'Oh no. The club staff do that.'

'Do they have to open the packets of biscuits? Put them on plates?'

'No, no. There's no manual labour involved. The staff do that.'

'So the committee of 20, of which I am being invited to be a member, will be responsible for choosing the biscuits?'

'Definitely. That would come within the remit of the Committee.' The secretary smiled at me. 'Can I put you down for that, then?'

'Oh I think so,' I said. 'I wouldn't miss it for the world.'

I had, before it had been explained to me exactly what my responsibilities would be, been reluctant to accept this position. A friend of mine had once claimed that anyone who wants to sit on a golf club committee has, by their very desire, proved themselves unfit to sit on a committee of any kind and should, therefore, be thrown out of office. My friend may well have been right but the promised joy of the experience was simply irresistible.

* * *

My Uncle Charles was a keen golfer though not, it has to be admitted, a terribly good one.

This assertion is supported by the fact that although my uncle was a member of the same club for 49 years and played golf at least twice a week and, towards the end of his life, considerably more often than that, he never managed to play rounds of sufficient quality to satisfy the requirements of the club's Handicap Committee, a feat which is made even more admirable when you realise that for 16 years he himself was a steadfast member of the Handicap Committee.

The only advice I can ever remember him giving me about golf was that if I ever took it up I should play with lots of balls.

'You mean play aggressively?' I said.

'No, no, no!' he said. 'I mean take lots of balls with you. I have to stuff my bag and my pockets with balls otherwise I'd never get round.'

He told me that an acquaintance of his called Mickey once won a match because his opponent ran out of balls. 'The chap Mickey was playing with wanted to buy a ball or two,' said Uncle Charles. 'Mickey offered to let him have a couple at £100 each but the chap refused to pay up and forfeited the match instead.' My uncle, who would have handed over his balls to anyone who needed them, said this was evidence that at his level balls are crucial. 'It doesn't matter what sort you have,' he said. 'With golf balls it's the quantity not the quality that counts.'

Charles held that there are two possible points of view about the people who sit on golf club committees.

The first is that such individuals are over-filled with a sense of public spirit, over-burdened with good will to all men and burning with such an intense joy that they have to drag themselves down to normality by spending several hours a week sitting in a stuffy, smoke-filled room listening to a bunch of excrescences arguing about nothing at great length.

The second is that at least 90% of those who sit on golf club committees have been genetically modified and have had their sense of humour removed and replaced with an enhanced sense of self-importance.

These were, I repeat, not my views but the views of my Uncle Charles and I give them here for whatever historical value they may be deemed to have.

Although not a great golfer, my Uncle Charles was a great committee man. And he definitely fell into the first category of committee members. He sat on committees, he once admitted, because he felt guilty about having such a wonderful life. He was married to, loved and was faithful to, a wonderful woman who loved and was faithful to him. He was not rich enough to have to worry about how to look after his money but he was well enough off never to have worry about not having enough of the stuff. He had no real skills but that lack was balanced by the fact that he had no real sense of ambition either and so the two balanced one another out neatly and the lack of skills never really troubled him.

He was, I suspect one of the very few people who have ever lived who genuinely believed that taking part is more important than winning. 'Spectators never win anything,' he once told me when I was about eleven and although he himself never won anything – not, as far as I know, even a Saturday night golf club raffle – he firmly believed in having a 'go' and no one I knew ever got as much out of failing as did my Uncle Charles.

For him, sitting on a committee was a sort of penance; a tip of the hat to the gods who had given him such a good life.

* * *

The first meeting of the Catering Committee Sub Committee (Billiards Room) which I attended was a good introduction to the strange world which I had entered.

The club had applied for a grant from the local Council two weeks before I was appointed. One of the club's Management Committees had thought it might be a good idea to persuade the Council to help pay for a new flagpole so that we could dignify any future Royal visits by flying the appropriate standard. (A surveyor sent by the Council had examined the club's existing flagpole and found it too full of woodworm to support the weight of a flag.)

Before deciding whether or not to make a contribution to our flagpole fund, the Council announced that it would be necessary to send one of its representative to all committee meetings held by the club to make sure that everything we did was politically correct.

As a result, my first experience of committee life was both entertaining and illuminating.

'Our first task this evening is to choose the biscuits for future Billiard Room Committee meetings,' announced our chairman for the evening. (Actually, he insisted on being called our chairperson but I find it difficult to believe that anyone will take this volume seriously if I write a book including a 'chairperson'.)

'I'm afraid that the last time we tried to decide which biscuits to buy we simply couldn't agree,' he explained.

'Does that mean that we don't have any biscuits for this meeting?' asked a woman in a yellow trouser suit.

'I'm afraid it probably does,' admitted the chairman.

The woman in the yellow trouser suit proposed a vote condemning the committee for failing to organise appropriate refreshments for itself. This vote was narrowly carried. As a newcomer, who hadn't attended the previous meeting, I abstained.

Once this unpleasant task had been completed the chairman suggested that we try harder to make a decision about which biscuits to select.

'What about ginger nuts?' suggested a man in a checked sports coat. The coat was made from something that looked like tweed but wasn't. It had orange and yellow checks and a brown leather piping down the lapels. I suspect that it might well have been luminous too. 'Everyone likes ginger nuts.'

'I think some members of the Council would find that term rather offensive,' said the Council's representative, a thin, grey-faced woman in a dark grey suit.

'I don't quite understand,' said the man in the sports coat.

The Council's representative sighed, as though tired of having to explain the obvious. 'The term 'ginger nut' is often used to describe persons with red hair,' she replied. 'People with red hair find that sort of label quite offensive.'

'But we don't have any red-headed members that I can think

of,' said the man in the sports coat.

'Most of our members haven't got much hair of any colour,' said a jolly, red-faced fellow in a blazer, grey flannels, white shirt and regimental tie.

'That isn't relevant,' snapped the grey-faced woman in the dark grey suit.

'What about Garibaldis?' suggested the woman in the yellow trouser suit.

'Those curious little biscuits full of dead flies?' said a fat man who wore an angora jumper and a full beard. He shivered. 'I hate them.'

'We would be unable to countenance the purchase of Garibaldi biscuits,' said the grey-faced woman. 'The name would almost certainly give offence to Italians or to follicularly challenged males. The Council has a policy of doing everything it can to improve relations with other European countries. We are at the moment negotiating to twin the town with an industrial centre in Northern Italy.'

'What did she say?' demanded the fat man.

'I think she said that Garibaldi biscuits might upset bald Italians,' explained the chairman.

'Do you know any bald Italians?' asked the fat man.

The chairman said he couldn't think of any off hand. The woman in the yellow trouser suit said she'd once stayed in a hotel in Venice where the night porter was follicularly challenged but added that she rather thought that he might have been Polish.

'Rich tea can't offend anyone, surely?' said a skinny woman in huge spectacles.

'Oh dear me no, we couldn't support the purchase of rich tea biscuits,' said the council's representative. 'The word 'rich' would give serious offence to many of our electors. We are very mindful of our responsibilities to the less privileged sections of the community.'

'I rather like jammy dodgers,' I said. 'Do you have any objection to jammy dodgers?'

'People on social security or sickness benefit would find that term totally unacceptable,' said the woman with the grey face.

She shivered and looked at me as though she would like to see me strung up.

'Lemon puffs?' suggested the man in the sports coat. 'I like lemon puffs.'

The woman with the grey face glowered at him and shook her head so violently that one of her ethnic earrings fell out. 'Lemon puffs would certainly not be acceptable,' she said. 'The term would give grave offence to our growing gay and lesbian community.'

There was some embarrassment at this. The man in the sports coat opened his mouth as though about to say something and then shut it again. He looked around, thought for a moment and then lowered his head. 'I'd never thought of a lemon puff as an offensive biscuit,' he said. 'I feel really bad now.' He looked bad too.

'Are bourbons acceptable?' asked the woman in the yellow trouser suit. She was a game woman who clearly didn't give up easily.

'Oh dear me no,' said the woman from the council. 'The link to the continental Bourbon family is most offensive and would cause considerable distress among many of our European friends.'

'Chocolate fingers?' suggested the fat man.

'Racist,' said the fat man firmly. He held out a hand, wiggled his fingers and hummed the first line of 'Ole Man River'.

The grey-faced woman shot him a look that would have turned a lesser being to stone. 'Exactly,' she said. 'We like to avoid the word 'chocolate' whenever possible.'

'Shortbread?'

'Offensive to short people.'

'Penguins?'

'The vegetarians wouldn't like that.'

'What about custard creams?'

There was a long silence.

All of us thought hard. None of us could think of a reason to disqualify custard creams. We all looked at the woman from the Council. She too was thinking hard. She nodded. 'Custard creams would be acceptable,' she admitted. She seemed unhappy that we had found a solution. 'As long as they are purchased from a council approved supplier and don't come from Burma.'

'Why can't they come from Burma?' asked the fat man.

'The Council has instituted a unilateral ban on imports from Burma.'

'Do they make custard creams in Burma?' asked the fat man.

No one knew.

'Does anyone actually like custard creams?' asked the woman in the yellow trouser suit.

It seemed that no one did, though we all agreed that they were better than nothing.

'They're all we're going to get,' said the chairman. 'Can we take a vote on custard creams?'

We voted and decided that custard creams would be the authorised biscuits for the Billiard Room Committees. The chairman then announced that at our next meeting we would discuss the type of tea we would choose to accompany the custard creams.

'I would like to propose a vote congratulating the committee on its hard work and on its success in choosing a suitable biscuit,' said the woman in the yellow trouser suit.

We voted to applaud ourselves. The chairman then banged a wooden gavel on the table and announced that the meeting was over.

'Please vacate the room as quickly as possible,' he said, looking at his watch. 'There's a meeting of the Billiards Room Committee Home Fixtures Sub-Committee in here in less than five minutes.'

We all got up and left.

Except for the grey-faced woman. She stayed behind to sit on the next committee meeting as the Council's representative.

'At least we'll get custard creams next time,' I said to the fat man as we left.

He looked at me as if I was mad. 'No chance,' he said. 'We've got to decide how many to buy, where to buy them from, what brand to choose and what sort of plate to put them on.'

'Oh,' I said.

'It could be years before we see a custard cream,' he said.

Chapter Fifteen

'He's Not Heavy. He's Our President.'

John, our club president, was widely disliked and he well deserved his lack of popularity.

Officially, John earned his living as a planning officer with the local Council, though his relatively high position in an over-staffed, under-worked department meant that he was able to spend most of his time at the golf club. None of his underlings at the office ever dared complain about his frequent absences and most councillors were terrified that if they protested he would find some way to make their lives miserable.

John loved rules and regulations and his main purpose in life was making life difficult for other people. He was not dishonest in the way that so many planning officers are. He didn't take bribes, accept free foreign holidays or spend his evenings in lap dancing clubs where he could be corrupted by fleshy pleasures. John was just bloody-minded and seemed to take particular delight out of making people unhappy. He was proud of the number of small businesses which he had forced into bankruptcy and would happily relate stories of how he had prevented innocent citizens from adding bedrooms to their homes. He loved nothing more than to push through a compulsory purchase order and to then follow it through by demolishing a cottage to make way for an unnecessary road widening scheme. He regarded all entrepreneurs as his enemies.

At the golf club John was always introducing new rules and the club noticeboard was forever thick with memos detailing new regulations which he had chosen to impose. He did this quite arbitrarily for he had discovered that his position as club president gave him the authority to create new regulations whenever he felt like it. Although the regulations he created had to be confirmed by various club committees, and occasionally even at the club's Annual General Meeting, he surmised, accurately, that because there would never be time to discuss all his regulations they would remain active indefinitely. It was thanks to John that men wearing red socks were not allowed into the clubhouse, that women had to wear skirts or dresses which reached at least three inches below their knees and that defacing notices on the club noticeboard had become a crime punishable by expulsion.

I once asked Simon how someone who was so unpopular had become club president.

'Fear,' replied Simon instantly. 'No one dared stand against him. We all have jobs, businesses or homes in the area.'

'But he can't have that much power,' I protested.

'Oh he does,' insisted Simon. 'Take Keith for example. He is very popular and would have made an excellent club president. But he runs a bakery. If he'd stood against John his life wouldn't have been worth living. John would have found some reason to close down the bakery.'

'Then there is Robert. He's a manager of one of the biggest local factories. They're expanding and they want permission to build another factory. If he had stood against John the planning application would have been turned down. And John would have made sure that Robert's bosses knew that it was his fault.'

'But he can't do that!'

'Oh yes he can,' said Simon. 'The planning rules are very complicated. He can always find something in the small print to use. He's been president for six years now. Three years ago a member called Tim stood against him. Nice chap. Retired. He thought he'd be safe because he was retired. But John suddenly and unexpectedly gave a national building company planning permission to erect a block of flats on some waste land right next to Tim's bungalow. Tim and his wife were driven mad by the noise. They sold up and moved away.'

* * *

John believed that his position in the club gave him the right to sit wherever he liked. On big, international golfing occasions, when the lounge was full of members eager to watch the professionals show just how it should be done, he would position a chair directly in front of the television set and settle himself down in it. The rest of us would be left to peer around his head as best we could.

But it wasn't the opacity of his head which troubled us most. It was the snoring. Since quite a few of the members tended to fall asleep in the club's comfortable chairs, snoring was something we were all pretty much accustomed to. But John's snoring always seemed louder and more intrusive than anyone else's.

Things came to a head one summer's day when the lounge was crowded with members anxious to watch the final few holes of the Open Championship on the television set.

'Turn up the sound a bit,' cried someone. 'I can't hear the television for the damned racket John is making.' I don't know whether it was a result of something he'd eaten or the way he was slumped in his chair but John was snoring particularly loudly that day.

'It's as loud as it will go,' replied the member who had commandeered the remote control device and who was, therefore, temporarily in charge of the television set.

'Well I can't hear the television,' complained the member who had moaned. 'All I can hear is John.'

It quickly became clear that the member who had moaned was not alone in being unable to listen to the television commentary above John's incessant snoring.

'If I was married to him I'd make him sleep in the spare room,' said Oliver.

'If I was married to him I'd tie a concrete block to his ankles and make him sleep in the pond behind the 16th,' said Gerald.

'Actually, that's not a bad idea,' said Simon.

'Do you think we could get away with it?' asked Gerald. 'Drop him in the pond? Does anyone have a concrete block spare?'

'No. Not in the pond,' said Simon. 'But why don't we move him outside. It's quite warm. He's asleep. He won't mind.'

The only objection to this came from a lady member who felt

certain that John would wake up if we tried to move him. 'If I as much as nudge my husband when he's snoring he's awake in an instant,' she said.

'If he does wake up he'll stop snoring,' Simon pointed out.

'We can't lose,' said Gerald, summarising the situation quite accurately.

We decided that the best thing to do was to lift John up in his chair, carry him out through the French windows and take him out onto the terrace. Since I was one of the few members not crippled by arthritis or a bad back I found myself one of the four people clutching a corner of John's leather armchair. Gerald and Simon picked up the small table upon which John had put his gin, his packet of small cigars, his lighter and his reading glasses and carried that behind us.

We got out through the French doors and onto the terrace with no difficulty whatsoever. We must have made a neat looking procession.

'Take him further,' yelled a voice from inside. 'We can still hear him in here.'

'Let's take him to the other side of the hill on the second hole,' suggested one of the other three chair bearers. 'He's not heavy.'

'He's not heavy, he's our president,' added another bearer.

And so we carried John the length of the first fairway, past the second tee, down the first hundred and fifty yards of the second fairway and onto a small grassy patch by the side of a stream which runs between the second and third holes.

We left him there and hurried back to the clubhouse.

* * *

When John walked into the clubhouse later that evening he did not, at first, say a word about waking up and finding himself out on the course instead of in the lounge. He just walked up the bar and ordered a large gin. Red-faced with rage he looked around as though trying to pick out the culprits. We all ignored him.

Until Gerald spoke.

'Where have you been, John?' he asked. 'We missed you.'

'I've been out on the course, sitting in a chair,' replied John angrily.

Gerald looked concerned. 'I'm surprised at you, John,' he said sternly. 'As you know there is a club rule prohibiting members from taking furniture out of the clubhouse.'

John stared at him, as though not believing what he was hearing. The rule, he and we all knew, had been introduced by John himself after several members had taken armchairs out onto the patio on a particularly warm summer evening.

'It's a serious infringement of the club rules,' said Simon.

John protested at this obvious injustice but the words just wouldn't come out properly. He made noises like a motor mower trying to start. He looked around. No one else spoke. No one muttered a word in his defence.

'The action was in deliberate violation of the clubhouse regulation which forbids members to take clubhouse furniture out of the building,' said Gerald.

Still no one said a word.

'I really think you should reconsider your position as club president,' said Oliver. 'You will remember that you have in the past required members to resign when they have violated club rules.'

John looked around the room. No one looked away. Everyone met his gaze.

'I think you should resign, John,' said Rupert. Astonished, we all stared at Rupert.

John put down his gin and opened his mouth. Nothing came out. He tried again. 'I'm not staying here,' he said. And he walked out.

The four of us who had carried John out to the second hole went out and brought back the chair and the table. John's lighter, a cheap disposable plastic thing, was still lying on the table alongside his empty glass. He had taken his spectacles and cigars. We posted the lighter to him at the planning office.

For a while we expected some sort of retaliation – either aimed at us as individuals or at the club. But John had been defeated. We never heard from him again.

However, various committees are still kept busy repealing the many laws which John introduced.

Chapter Sixteen

'Sunny And Dry.'

'I can only manage nine holes,' said Oliver, rushing up to join us on the tee.

'Are you playing like that?' Simon asked him.

'Why not?' demanded Oliver. 'It's about time one of us tried to offer a fashion lead.' He was wearing a pair of pinstriped trousers, a matching waistcoat, a pale blue shirt, the cuffs of which were fastened with gold links and a dark blue tie which had pale blue spots all over it.

'Those look like the trousers to your best suit,' said Gerald.

'Well spotted,' said Oliver. 'It is.' He thought for a moment. 'They are.'

'Where's the jacket?'

'I didn't think I could play in a jacket,' said Oliver. 'So it's hanging up in the car.'

'What happened to those old green corduroy trousers you were wearing the other day?'

'I just thought it was time for one of us to make a bit of an effort,' said Oliver who is, in truth, usually the most elegant of us.

'Where are you going in such a hurry?' asked Simon.

Oliver sighed. 'I've got an important meeting with some chaps from London at four,' he said. 'I'll just have time for nine holes if I don't bother changing. I can't turn up to a meeting in green cords with a golf tee behind my ear. I don't think London people approve of us playing golf during working hours.'

'I wouldn't play in my best suit,' said Simon. 'I'd be worried I'd snag it in the brambles or get it wet and muddy.'

'I won't be playing into any brambles,' said Oliver. 'And I'm not going to get wet and muddy. I got home last Saturday and Cynthia didn't believe I'd been playing golf at all. She thought I must be having an affair with some woman. She went over my clothes with a magnifying glass and said there were no signs of my having played golf in them. I'm a very clean and tidy player.' He thought for a moment. 'And if my ball should accidentally bounce into brambles one of you guys can wade in and get it for me.'

'What if it rains?' asked Simon.

'I checked the weather forecast,' Oliver assured him. 'They've guaranteed a lovely sunny afternoon.'

'Not even covered themselves with the usual warning about scattered showers?' asked Gerald.

'Sunny and dry,' said Oliver. 'The chap who does the weather on the radio said it was one of those days for sitting on the patio with a Pimms and a good book.'

* * *

When Oliver, Gerald, Simon and I set off the sky was blue, the sun was shining and the day looked set fair. The few fluffy little white clouds which decorated the sky looked harmless and unthreatening.

Naturally, by the time we had completed three holes, it had started to rain. It wasn't raining hard. Just drizzle. It was, as usual, the sort of stuff you don't really notice until you realise that you are too soaked to bother with waterproofs or an umbrella.

'Maybe I should go back,' said Oliver, looking up. 'I don't want to turn up to this meeting looking damp.'

'You can borrow my waterproofs, if you like,' offered Gerald, generously.

Oliver looked up at the sky, thought for a moment, and shook himself, rather like a dog shaking rain from his coat. 'Thanks,' he said. 'But I'll be fine – I've got an umbrella.'

Now none of us usually bother with umbrellas on the golf course. There are two reasons for this. The first is that our course tends to be rather on the windy side and so when wind and rain come together the rain usually falls horizontally rather than vertically. An umbrella is of limited value against such a downpour – particularly when the wind is likely to change direction every few seconds. The second reason is that the sort of wind we usually get tends to destroy umbrellas. We therefore regarded Oliver's 'I'll be fine – I've got an umbrella' as rather akin to hearing the Captain of the Titanic dismiss warnings of an iceberg ahead by saying: 'We'll be fine – I've got a kettle of hot water.'

Oliver dismissed our reservations with a wave of the hand. His umbrella was, he told us with pride, a specially designed Swiss model with doubled-jointed struts which enabled it to bend with the wind. According to Oliver, the people who had sold it to him at Zurich airport had assured him that even if it blew itself inside out it could easily be put back into shape with a flick of the wrist.

By the time we had finished the fourth hole the sky had turned black, the heavens had opened, the rain was coming down in torrents and the constituent parts of Oliver's umbrella had been abandoned in a rubbish bin. It had taken the wind less than five seconds to separate the double thickness silk cover from the aluminised rustless patented double-jointed struts. Few things are quite as utterly useless as a broken umbrella and Oliver had thrown away his expensive protection with a mixture of anger, frustration and contempt. He was angry with himself for having fallen for the shop assistant's promises, frustrated by the fact that the umbrella had failed and contemptuous of the company which had made the thing in the first place.

'I know what I'll do,' said Oliver, kicking off his shoes and removing his trousers. 'I'll take off my clothes before they get any wetter and put them into the big pocket at the front of my bag. They'll be snug and dry in there. When we get back to the clubhouse I can give myself a quick wipe down with a towel, get dressed and go to the meeting without anyone noticing a thing.'

He rolled up his trousers and pushed them into his golf bag, then removed his waistcoat, tie and shirt and crammed them in too. He rolled his socks into a ball and stuffed them into the golf bag on top of the waistcoat, tie, shirt and trousers. He then put his golf shoes back on.

The golf course had been quiet when we'd set out. Most

members present had been sitting on the terrace with a Pimms and a good book each. The bad weather meant that the course was now deserted. Gerald, Simon and I were the only other people around and we had no objections to Oliver playing golf wearing only his underpants and a pair of golf shoes. It seemed a good idea.

Looking back through time, it now seems likely that things would have continued to go satisfactorily if Oliver had not hooked his next shot over the hedge and sent his ball bouncing along the road which runs alongside that part of the course.

'I can see my ball,' insisted Oliver, climbing over the padlocked five-barred gate which separates the golf course from the world outside. 'You play on,' he called cheerily. 'I'll meet you on the green.'

We carried on, as did the rain.

But when we arrived on the next green there was no sign of Oliver. We stood in the pouring rain and waited in vain for him to arrive.

'I hope he's all right,' said Gerald, gloomily. His hair was plastered to his skull and rain dripped off the end of his nose.

'It's a busy road,' said Simon. 'There's a supermarket on the other side of it. There is a lot of traffic along here. I hope nothing's happened to him.'

'Perhaps we should go and take a look,' Gerald suggested. 'He might be lying in the road. Injured perhaps. Maybe unconscious.'

Naturally, when such gloomy thoughts have been aired they cannot easily be forgotten. Increasingly concerned we waited another few minutes and then we left our golf bags where they were and headed for a small gap in the hedge which was used by local dog owners whose animals use the golf course as a lavatory. Getting through the gap wasn't easy and Simon tore his waterproof jacket rather badly. 'He'd better be lying in a pool of blood, when we find him,' he said rather crossly, though I don't believe he meant this. It was, I suspect, just something that he blurted out in the heat of the moment.

There was absolutely no sign of Oliver. He had disappeared.

Gerald and Simon walked up the road in one direction and I walked down the road in the other. The road was straight. There was no shelter and there were no hiding places. We then retraced our steps and met up again.

'Nothing,' said Simon.

'No sign of him down there,' I confirmed.

'Maybe we'd better go back to the green,' suggested Gerald. 'Perhaps he's there.'

We wriggled through the gap in the hedge again. This time it was my time to rip my waterproof jacket. 'Damn Oliver,' I said rather more forcefully than I had meant to. 'This is all his fault.'

We finished the hole and carried on towards the next tee. But our hearts were no longer in the game. We kept looking over our shoulders, expecting to see Oliver come running up towards us. It was impossible to work out where he could have gone to.

We finished the round. But it was difficult to concentrate. At any moment we expected to see Oliver come bounding up to us like a dog who has run off on his own and is returning to an anxious master. But Oliver did not come bounding up to us and we remained anxious.

There was no sign of Oliver back at the golf club either. We showered, dried ourselves, changed and ordered drinks in the bar. Still he didn't turn up.

'Maybe he just came back to the club and went off to his meeting,' suggested Simon.

'If he did, his car would have gone,' said Gerald.

'I'll go and look,' I offered. I went and looked. Oliver's car was still there. I was shivering and soaked again by the time I got indoors. The weather had deteriorated still further. It was really not a good day to be wandering about the countryside dressed only in a pair of golf shoes and a pair of white, Y-front underpants.

We waited.

And waited.

At nine o'clock that evening the barman came to tell Gerald that there was a telephone call for him.

'It was Oliver's wife,' he said, when he returned to our table. He looked worried. 'Oliver hasn't arrived back home and he didn't get to his meeting. Someone apparently rang Oliver's wife to ask where he was. The poor woman is tearing her hair out with worry.'

'We'd better ring the hospital,' said Gerald quietly. 'I'll go.'

He was away twenty minutes. He shook his head as he came back. 'No-one of his description has been admitted to the hospital.'

Just then the barman came back and asked for Gerald. It was Oliver's wife again.

'She rang the police station,' said Gerald. 'She asked if they'd seen a lost golfer. The police apparently said that the only golfer they had in custody was one wearing nothing but a pair of golf shoes and a pair of damp underpants.'

We all sighed with relief. This was clearly Oliver.

'Ah,' said Simon. 'What did Oliver's wife tell them?'

'She said she thought that might be him,' said Gerald. 'And rang to ask if we would pop along and take a look. She said she'd have gone herself if she hadn't drunk a bottle of sherry in order to calm her nerves. She said that if she turned up reeking of sherry they'd probably let Oliver go and arrest her.'

And that's how we found Oliver. And how, eventually, we found out what had happened to him.

* * *

'I could see my ball,' Oliver told us all later that evening after we'd got him back home and reunited him with his loved one. 'It had bounced on the road, over the pavement which ran between the road and the supermarket, over a low wall around the supermarket and into their car park. I spotted a supermarket trolley lying on its side on the pavement and since the strap of my bag was rubbing on my shoulder I decided to pop my golf bag into the trolley and push it along to where my ball was lying. I thought I could probably play the ball as it lay. It was sitting up quite well on the road and I thought that if I played a decent seven iron I could get the ball back over the hedge and onto the fairway.'

'It was,' he said, 'at that point that a fat woman with two kids came out of the supermarket pushing a trolley laden with cornflakes and toilet rolls. She took one look at me and screamed. At first I couldn't work out why she was screaming and then I remembered that to her I might have looked a little odd.'

'It's probably not every day the poor woman spots a bloke dressed only in underpants and golf shoes pushing a golf bag in a trolley through the car park at the supermarket,' said Simon.

'She probably thought she'd been overdoing the cooking sherry,' said Gerald.

Oliver's wife made a choking sound.

'So what did you do?' I asked.

'I had to make a pretty quick decision,' said Oliver. 'I could either abandon my ball, count it as lost, and head straight back for the golf course or I could play my ball where it lay and then run for it. I decided that since if I did the former I'd have to go all the way back to the tee and drive off again I would totter over to my ball as quickly as I could, play it and then run for it.'

'Bad decision?' asked Gerald.

'It was, as it turned out, a bad decision,' agreed Oliver. 'I would have been all right but the woman who'd screamed had darted back into the supermarket and alerted the store manager. He sent out two of his finest security operatives who appeared from nowhere. I would have got away from them if I hadn't had the trolley and my bag,' he sighed, shook his head and pulled his dressing gown around him tighter. 'The trolley wobbled a lot and had a definite tendency to swerve to the right but even so all went well until the wheels locked. The damned thing was fitted with one of those devices which locks the wheels when the trolley is taken outside the supermarket car park.'

The security operatives who captured Oliver locked him in a tiny office inside the supermarket and called the police. The police overreacted wildly. Suspecting from the tone of the telephone call they had received that Oliver was on a suicide mission and was planning to use a golf bag stuffed with explosives to blow up the supermarket the police despatched four police cars, two ambulances, a fire engine, an armed response unit, three photographers, their own video cameraman and two television crews. Within five minutes the supermarket was surrounded. Within ten minutes Oliver was wrapped in a blanket and being cross-examined by a pair of suspicious senior detectives who rather fancied themselves as future recruits to Special Branch.

Oliver, unabashed, demanded a telephone, a lawyer and his MP. He said he would be writing to the newspapers, the United

Nations, the European Union, the International Court at La Hague and the golf club's main Catering Committee (of which he was deputy chairman).

None of these requests or threats did any good at all. The police took as much notice of Oliver as they would have done of any other semi-naked vagrant lunatic and it took him several hours to convince his interrogators that he was not a criminal but was instead a respectable, middle-aged man who had a perfectly rational explanation for why he came to be racing through a supermarket car park pushing a wobbly shopping trolley, clad only in a pair of sodden underpants and a pair of golf shoes.

Our arrival tipped the balance in his favour and once the police had convinced themselves that Oliver was not a terrorist (the report from the bomb squad had gone some way towards confirming Oliver's claims) and had checked that none of the local lunatic asylums had lost any patients, they decided that charging him with indecent exposure and the attempted theft of a supermarket trolley (the only two charges they could think of) might result in some pretty sarcastic newspaper headlines. They told him not to do it again and said that he could go.

At that point Oliver rather lost his presence of mind.

'I wish to make a formal complaint,' he said when he had taken his creased trousers out of his golf bag and put them back on. Properly trousered he looked and clearly felt far more confident.

Stunned, we said nothing.

The police inspector to whom Oliver addressed his complaint stared disbelievingly.

'When I was dragged from the supermarket car park,' complained Oliver. 'I asked the security guards to let me mark my ball. They refused.'

The inspector continued to stare.

'I think we should get out of here,' muttered Gerald quietly.

Simon and I picked Oliver up and carried him out of the police station. Gerald took his golf clubs.

'Thanks for everything,' called Simon as we hurried away.

I turned to look. The policeman was opening and shutting his mouth but nothing was coming out.

* * *

By the time Oliver had finished his story his wife was asleep. Exhaustion, anxiety and sherry had done their job. She was lying on her back, mouth open, snoring daintily.

'I'm going to sue the bloody weather forecaster,' said Oliver. 'It was all his fault.'

Simon stood up. Gerald and I followed suit.

'We're going home,' said Simon wearily. 'Go to bed, Oliver!'

'And be grateful it's your bed and not a cot in a prison cell,' said Gerald.

'I suppose you're right,' said Oliver. He thought for a minute or two. 'But that ball was sitting up nicely, you know.' He paused and thought again. 'With a decent five iron I could have got it back onto the fairway.'

'Goodnight Oliver,' said Gerald. We headed for the door.

'I might go back tomorrow and try that shot from the car park,' Oliver said.

We left.

Chapter Seventeen

'My Wife And I Only Ever Argue When She Is Being Unreasonable.'

The comfortable leather armchairs and slightly battered brass-topped tables had all been pushed up against the walls of the lounge. In their places someone had arranged several rows of old-fashioned chairs made of metal tubing and faded green canvas. Approximately a third of the chairs were already occupied. I looked around and spotted Simon sitting by himself at the end of one of the rows.

'Sit down,' he said. 'I saved three chairs.' The chairs next to his were occupied, respectively, by a hat, a scarf and a folded newspaper.

'What's going on?' I asked, squeezing past him and sitting down. Simon looked at me. 'Haven't you had a letter?'

I shook my head.

'It's the Annual General Meeting.' Simon slipped a hand inside his jacket, pulled out a folded letter and handed it to me. The letter was an invitation to attend the club's AGM.

'Read the P.S. at the bottom of the page,' said Simon, leaning across and pointing a finger at a sentence at the bottom of the letter.

I read the P.S.

'Please let me know if you do not receive this communication.'

'How...?' I began.

'Exactly!' said Simon, with a big grin. 'Wonderful, isn't it?'

'How long do these things last?' I asked. I have a low boredom threshold and usually try to avoid meetings of any kind.

'They usually break up at about half past one or two,' replied Simon. 'But last year's meeting was closed down by the police at about ten.'

'Two in the morning?' I asked.

'Best entertainment of the year,' Simon assured me.

'And last year?'

'There was a lengthy argument about whether spikes should be allowed on the course. The chairman of the Greens Committee claimed that if no one wore spikes it would be easier to keep the greens in good condition but not everyone was happy. One chap complained that he liked the clatter of spikes on the concrete path outside the clubhouse. 'It sounds like hail on a tin roof,' I remember him saying. 'I find it very soothing and reassuring.'

'So what happened?' I asked.

'Some woman who is a lawyer said that if we banned spikes everyone who fell over would sue the club,' said Simon. 'Another lawyer said that he loathed lawyers who made money out of accidents. The first lawyer threw an ashtray at the second lawyer. The second lawyer thumped her. Then the first lawyer pulled a seven iron out from underneath her chair and started beating the other lawyer around the head.' He grinned. 'It's bound to be a long evening again so I made sure that we got seats near to the bar.'

In the few minutes that I'd been there the number of empty seats had diminished rapidly. Simon and I had had to fight hard to protect the seats which he had reserved for Oliver and Gerald. It was with some relief that we saw them arrive.

'I'll get in some drinks before the rush starts,' said Gerald, making his way to the bar while Oliver removed Simon's scarf from one of the spare seats on my left and sat down.

'Make them trebles,' called Simon to Gerald. He rubbed his hands together in gleeful expectation.

'This is the only meeting of the year I would never miss,' Oliver told me. 'I was in Turkey on holiday two years ago and flew back three days early for the AGM.' He shook his head as if still hardly believing the memory. 'And you should have been here last year. It was a short meeting but pretty damned exciting I can tell you.'

'I heard about it.'

'You should have seen the lawyer trying to brain the other lawyer with an eight iron. Brilliant.'

'It was a seven iron,' said Simon.

'Eight iron.'

I held up a hand. 'Six iron?' I suggested.

They paused for a moment then both nodded. 'Six iron,' they agreed.

'Do you remember that chap trying to split open the skull of the chairman of the Greens Committee with a billiard cue?' asked Oliver.

'I could never work out where he got the billiard cue from,' said Simon.

'Then the Ladies' Captain and that woman with the purple bouffant hair started fighting.'

'At what point were the police called?' I asked.

'I think it was when the temporary barman threw the best part of a pint of mild and bitter over that chap with a glass eye whose name I can never remember,' said Simon.

Before Oliver could reply Gerald came back clutching four drinks. By the time these had been handed round, and Gerald had handed Simon back his hat, and had settled himself down on the seat which the hat had occupied, the club secretary was calling for order and banging the table in front of him with the sort of wooden mallet normally used for knocking tent pegs into the ground. 'We've got a lot to get through this evening,' he said. 'So I'll introduce your club chairman who will start the proceedings without further ado.' The club secretary then sat down and for a minute or so nothing happened. Then the club secretary stood up again. 'We appear to have temporarily mislaid the club chairman,' he announced. 'So, in view of the length of the agenda I will invite the deputy club chairman to take over until he appears.' He then sat down and as though sitting on the other end of a see-saw the deputy club chairman stood up, thanked the secretary, welcomed us all, read out a long and utterly boring list of apologies from local dignitaries (I didn't catch any of the names or indeed any of their reasons for not attending but I did notice that the mayor, the deputy mayor, the chairman of the local planning committee, the chief constable and a bishop were among those who had, for some reason been invited and had, for no doubt far better reasons, declined the invitation) and an even longer list of even more boring apologies from club members who were, presumably, too nervous, too old or too disabled to risk attending.

'The first item on our agenda this evening,' said the deputy club chairman, after he had completed this dull but obligatory task, 'is to discuss the problem of slow play.' He paused and cleared his throat. 'Personally,' he began, 'and speaking as a member rather than in my official capacity, I would like to say that I don't know what all the fuss is about. Golf is a game most of us play for entertainment or relaxation and I can't see why anyone would want to hurry it up and get it over with as quickly as possible.'

'Mr Acting Chairman, there would be far less slow play if the greenkeeper was instructed to get rid of all the rough,' said a florid-faced man I'd never seen before. 'I spend around five minutes a hole looking for my ball. That means that in a round of golf I spend an hour and a half stumbling around in the rough, ball hunting. If there was no rough I could cut ninety minutes off the time it takes me to play a round of golf.'

'We might as well fill in all the ponds and streams,' suggested a member who was wearing tartan trews, a green mohair sweater and a peaked cap with GOLF inscribed on the peak in gold embroidery. 'That would speed things up.'

'We could get round faster if the holes were shorter,' suggested a man in a check jacket.

To my surprise Gerald stood up. 'The people who design golf courses obviously never play golf or hate golfers or are psychopathic bastards or have some sort of ongoing contract with the people who make golf balls.' He paused and looked around. Many heads were nodding. 'The holes that win prizes are impossible to play,' he said. 'Who wants to play a 600 yard hole that is studded with ponds and bunkers and clever little twists and turns? The holes the golf magazines get excited about have water all down the left, thick trees all down the right, a fairway which is six feet wide and studded with bunkers which move about and a green which is shaped like an upturned saucer and as smooth as glass.' He paused again. More heads were nodding and the nodding was now being accompanied by so much murmuring of approval that the club lounge was beginning to look and sound like a convention centre for Buddhists. 'The ideal hole would be 150 yards long, all downhill, with smooth hard-as-concrete grass leading down to a dish-shaped green. There would be a fifty foot tall tower on every tee equipped with a lift. Players could then go to the top of the tower and hit their balls into a long chute which fed balls down onto the green. The hole would be two feet across. Every golfer would get a hole in one at every hole and we could play a round of golf in under an hour.'

A large man with a head the shape and size of a cannon ball turned round and glared at Gerald. 'Outrageous!' he bellowed. 'A hole two foot across would take all the skill out of the game. One foot diameter would be far more sensible and would ensure that skill was properly rewarded.'

I looked at Simon. He grinned.

'It's a good idea but, sadly, I don't think it would be practical,' objected a man in a check cap. 'In order to make the lifts work we would have to lay underground electricity cables all over the course.'

Gerald sat down, looked at us and shook his head slightly. He closed his eyes and put his head in his hands.

'Mr Acting Chairman,' said a member smoking a rosewood pipe. 'I think our problems would all be solved if we banned dentists from the course.' He put his pipe back into his mouth, sat down and folded his arms.

His suggestion was met with total silence as the assembled members tried to work out how banning dentists might solve the problem of slow play.

'Er, just how would this help stop the problem of slow play?' asked the deputy chairman after a while.

The member took his pipe out of his mouth and stood up. 'It seems to me that too many of our members are dentists,' he said. 'I know personally of at least five. If we ban them from the course we will reduce the pressure on tee times.' He sat down and, almost immediately stood up again. 'Besides,' he added, 'I find it depressing to see dentists on the course. I saw a whole group of them on the fifth green the other day. I was very distressed by the sight.' He looked around the room. 'I feel very strongly about this.'

Oliver leant closer to me. 'What would you call a group of dentists?' he whispered.

'I don't know,' I whispered back.

'An abscess,' he suggested.

'An abscess of dentists,' I said, trying it out. 'Sounds good,' I told him.

'I just thought of it,' he murmured, very pleased with himself.

'May I come back to the previous member's suggestion about getting rid of the rough?' asked a bald man who had a pair of tortoiseshell spectacles resting on the tip of his nose.

The chairman said he might.

'Well it seems to me that since most of us spend most of our time in the rough and very little time on the fairway we would all save a great deal of time and effort – not to mention balls – if we told the ground staff to let the fairways grow and to cut the rough.' He pushed his spectacles up his nose, looked around the room, and sat down.

As he sat down a tall, thin fellow holding a cigar stood up. 'We should do away with the handicapping system,' he said. 'Handicapping is nothing more than raw communism. It's an evil system. The idea of the handicapping system is to take from those who have and give to those who don't have. It's nothing more than communism,' he said. He sat down to silence.

A round fellow in a bright pink turtle neck sweater stood up. 'So why aren't the Russians and the Chinese any good at golf?' he wanted to know. 'Name me one good Russian golfer?'

The cigar smoker looked startled but said nothing.

'I would like to bring up the honours board,' said a man with bushy hair.

'We'll come to other business later on if you don't mind,' said the deputy chairman, who was, with some justification, concerned that he was losing control of the meeting.

'I won't be here later on,' said the man with the bushy hair. 'I've got to leave at nine. There's a programme I want to watch on the television and our video recorder has broken. My complaint is that my name on the honours board is in much smaller printing than anyone else's. It seems to me that this is a very obvious case of religious discrimination.'

'Er, what religion are you, Mr Protheroe-Shiplington-Bartram?' asked the acting chairman.

'I don't think that's any of your business,' replied Mr Protheroe-Shiplington-Bartram. 'But if you must know I'm a Methodist. I won last year's July Cup and was looking forward to seeing my name on the honours board in due prominence.'

The acting chairman turned round and studied the board which happened to be right behind him. 'Your name is on the board is it not?'

'Indeed it is, Mr Chairman. But in much smaller print size than anyone else's name.'

'I can speak about this with some knowledge,' said the acting chairman, 'since I am a member of the Honours Board Sub-Committee. You are quite right that your name is smaller than anyone else's but that is simply because your name is longer than anyone else's and there is only so much space available for each person on the honours board.'

'But when you've waited as long as I have to see your name on the honours board it is a bit of a blow to have to look at it through a magnifying glass to see that it's there at all.'

'Oh come now, Mr Protheroe-Shiplington-Bartram,' said the acting chairman. 'I think that's a bit of an exaggeration. The gold paint which we use for the honours board is quite expensive you know. We can only allocate so many brushfuls for each name.'

'Well I don't think it's good enough and unless my name is repainted the same size as everyone else's I intend to take this further,' said Mr Protheroe-Shiplington-Bartram. At this point he clearly intended to emphasise his passion by storming, or at least flouncing, out of the room. Unfortunately, the rows of chairs were crammed together so tightly that what had been intended to be a dramatic departure ended up as a rather apologetic litany of 'Excuse me's', 'Sorry about thats', 'Whoops, pardons' and 'If I could just squeeze through there, pleases'.

* * *

After Mr Protheroe-Shiplington-Bartram's departure the acting chairman attempted to return to the running order which the secretary had so carefully prepared before the meeting started. But the damage had been done. A woman with a safety pin through her nose stood up.

'While on the subject of discrimination,' she said. 'I want an explanation for what happened to Mr Ellwood.'

'Mr Ellwood?' said the acting chairman, who clearly had no idea who Mr Ellwood was or is.

'Mr Ellwood is disabled,' said the woman.

'Are you a member, madam?' asked the acting chairman.

'I represent Mr Ellwood,' said the woman.

'Is he here?'

'No. You won't let him play. I'm here on his behalf. I represent the anti-discrimination unit of the local social services department.'

'Point of order, Mr Acting Chairman,' said a man in a green corduroy suit. 'If this person is not a member she should not be allowed to speak at this meeting. Indeed, she shouldn't even be allowed in the building.'

'I represent the public,' said the woman with the safety pin holding her nose together. She turned round to snarl at the man in the green corduroy suit. 'It's unconstitutional to keep the public out. Under the Human Rights Act I have every right to be here.'

'Why, er, why do you claim that we won't let Mr Ellwood play?' asked the acting chairman, rather tentatively.

'He is legless and confined to a wheelchair,' said the woman with the safety pin through her nose. 'He was told that he couldn't play because of his wheelchair.'

'I'm afraid that being in a wheelchair would probably occasion some difficulties,' admitted the acting chairman, picking his words with some care.

'That's not the point,' said the woman. 'Mr Ellwood doesn't want to play your stupid game. But the point is that if he did he wouldn't be able to because the little flat green bit with the flag with a ten on it just before the stagnant pond can only be reached via three wooden steps.'

'I'm afraid...,' began the acting chairman.

'And the grass between the flags is, in many places, far too soft for a wheelchair.'

'I'm afraid I don't quite understand your point,' said the acting chairman at his most emollient.

'You're in breach of the legislation,' said the social worker triumphantly. 'You should lay down concrete paths and provide ramps as an alternative to steps.'

'I'm sorry you feel disappointed with our course,' said the acting chairman, 'but it seems to me that if Mr Ellwood has admitted that he doesn't actually want to play golf then any case he might bring would be built on shaky ground. Indeed, I would go so far as to suggest that he wouldn't have a leg to stand on.'

This unfortunate remark was doubtless not intended with any malice; it was simply one of those unfortunate slips of the tongue which afflict us all from time to time. But to the woman with the safety pin it was nothing less than a declaration of war. She stalked from the room indignantly, with froth forming at the corners of her mouth. We would, we were told, hear from her again. We suspected we would.

* * *

The acting chairman cleared his throat and rapped his knuckles on the table top. 'Now I call upon Sidney, the club treasurer and chairman of the Finance Sub-Committee to give us his annual financial report and, er, a full report of the club's financial position.'

Sidney, a small, bespectacled fellow who wore a grey suit enlivened by a bright red tie, pulled a battered leather briefcase up onto his lap, unfastened the two straps which held the case shut and pulled out a three inch thick wedge of papers. Sidney was a successful local businessman who ran a chain of discount stores. He was also a successful club golfer though it was alleged by some that he had achieved many of his victories only through his ability to knock 10% off his score without anyone noticing. As he struggled to refasten his briefcase and at the same time put the papers down on the table in front of him the papers slipped and fell to the floor. Another member knelt down and tried to pick the papers up.

'Don't worry too much,' Sidney reassured him merrily, 'they weren't in any particular order.' He cleared his throat. His audience sat forward, as silent and expectant as if they had been spectators lined up on the first tee waiting for the Sunday morning foursomes to begin.

'Er, well, thank you Mr Acting Chairman,' began Sidney. He cleared his throat again and picked up the top paper from the pile in front of him. 'As you all know,' he said, 'the amusement machine in the gentlemen's changing rooms has for many years been our major source of income.' He put down the piece of paper he was holding, which was an invoice for roofing felt, and slid it to the bottom of the pile. He rummaged around amongst his papers and produced another example from his collection. 'In the 1971-2 year our income from this machine paid for 32% of our expenditure on salaries, maintenance, electricity and grass seed. However, during the two decades which have followed our income from this source has fallen steadily while our costs have continued to rise.'

'Excuse me, Sidney,' said the acting chairman, who had noticed some fairly hectic arm waving on his right, 'but I rather think that Maurice wishes to make a point.' He would, in fact, have needed to have been blind not to have noticed Maurice's furious attempt to attract attention to himself.

Maurice, given his chance, opened and shut his mouth several times. 'I've forgotten what I was going to say,' he admitted, going very red.

'If the amusement machine still gave out a decent jackpot you'd find people wouldn't mind putting their money into it,' said Peregrine, taking advantage of Maurice's unfortunate lapse of memory to make a point of his own. 'Since you put a £5 limit on the jackpot most of the fellows have just stopped bothering. If you win the jackpot you're out of pocket by the time you've bought everybody a drink.'

'That's exactly the point I was going to make!' cried Maurice, at once both delighted that he no longer had to struggle to remember what it was that he was going to say and furious that he had not been the first to say it.

'Thank you, Maurice, thank you Peregrine,' said the acting chairman. 'Thank you gentlemen,' he added just in case he had missed anyone out. 'Sidney, would you like to continue?'

'Thank you, Mr Acting Chairman,' said Sidney. 'Very kind of you.' He pulled out another piece of paper. 'The price of grass seed has gone up by 765% in the last twelve months,' he announced. Apparently surprised by this figure he leant forwards and peered at the paper he was holding. There was much ooing and aahing at this and a great deal of breath was sucked in. 'I'm sorry,' he said, 'that should be 7.65%.' There was a pause while he shuffled through some more papers and Maurice took advantage of the delay in the proceedings to raise his arm in order to attract the attention of the acting chairman.

'I would like to propose a vote of thanks to the greenkeeping staff,' he said, when the acting chairman had invited him to speak. 'I think we are all grateful to them for their excellent work in maintaining the high standard of the course.'

'I'll second that,' said a man in a pin-striped suit and an ill-fitting brown toupee.

'Shall we vote on that then, gentlemen?' asked the acting chairman.

Hands were raised in support of the motion.

'That seems to be carried unanimously,' said the chairman.

'You didn't vote, Mr Chairman,' said Sidney.

'I don't think I have to vote unless there's a tie do I Sidney?' said the chairman.

'I think it's probably up to you, Mr Acting Chairman,' said Sidney. 'But I just thought I ought to mention it.'

'Then I'll vote for the motion,' said the acting chairman. 'Since there are no votes against that definitely makes it unanimous.'

A man in a pink jumper with a great deal of bouffant grey hair stood up. 'On behalf of the Greens Committee,' he said, 'I would like to thank the members for their kindness and generosity in making this statement at this time. We have, as most of you will be only too well aware, had a great deal to contend with during the last three months. The moles on the 13th green caused us all a good deal of concern and I know for a fact that the boggy patch beside the 16th green kept the head greenkeeper awake for much of last month.'

'Thank you,' said the acting chairman. 'Sidney, would you like to continue with your financial report?'

'Thank you Mr Chairman,' said Sidney. He cleared his throat, stood up and began again.

'Shall I go straight to the bottom line to save time?' asked Sidney.

'Splendid idea' said the acting chairman, with a broad smile on his face. 'I knew we could trust you to hit the nail on the head and call a spade a spade.'

'It's not terribly good,' said Sidney. 'We seem to be overdrawn,' he coughed and looked down. 'The, er, biggest problem is the number of unpaid membership fees.'

This news was greeted in total silence. No one wanted to comment. The acting chairman suddenly took a serious interest in his fingernails. The club secretary had a slight coughing fit. Other members spotted something on the floor that needed their attention or found that their watches needed winding. Pens were taken out and cleaned and noses were blown.

'We need to look at some innovative ways of raising money,' suggested Sidney. 'I propose that we look at the possibility of selling advertising on our grass.'

No one said anything probably because none of us were quite sure that we had heard what we thought we had heard.

'They do it at cricket grounds,' said Sidney. 'They sell advertising space to all sorts of companies.' He paused and then, mistaking the continued silence for enthusiasm, continued. 'We have far more grass than cricket clubs have,' he said. 'We have 18 greens to sell – not to mention all the fairways.' Once again he paused. Once again there was silence. 'We could allow advertisers to sponsor individual bunkers,' he suggested.

'Mr Acting Chairman, will you please call the police and an ambulance,' said a short thin man in a blue short-sleeved sweater and a yellow shirt. He moved purposefully towards Sidney.

'Why shall I say I'm calling?' asked the acting chairman taking out his mobile telephone.

'The police will need to arrest me for murder,' said the man in the yellow shirt. 'And the ambulance will be needed to take away the body.'

Sidney headed for the door. The man in the yellow shirt started to follow, hesitated, stopped, retraced his steps and sat down again. Several people reached across to pat him on the back.

* * *

'I want to complain about the use of bad language by male members,' said a large woman in a pink trouser suit and a pink flowery hat.

'Can we deal with that later on?' asked the acting chairman.

'No,' said the woman in pink. 'If you don't deal with it now you won't get your shirts ironed for a week.'

'That's his wife,' Oliver muttered. 'She's scary.'

Torn between establishing his authority and wearing wrinkled shirts for a week, the acting chairman hesitated.

'I was having tea on the terrace when I distinctly heard a man say a rude word,' said the acting chairman's wife.

'What word was that?' asked the acting chairman.

'I've no intention of repeating the word in front of all these people!'

'Would you write it down?'

'Give me a piece of paper and a pencil.'

The acting chairman handed his wife a piece of paper and a pencil. His wife took them both, rested the piece of paper against the side of her handbag and then hesitated, pencil poised. 'I'm not sure how to spell it,' she confessed.

'You'll have to tell me what the word is, my dear,' said the acting chairman. 'I can't tell you how to spell it unless you tell me what it is.'

'Bollocks,' said the woman in pink going red.

The acting chairman told his wife how to spell the word. She wrote it down and handed him the piece of paper and his pencil.

'Do you know the name of the member responsible for this outrage?' the acting chairman asked his wife.

His wife, the woman in pink, looked embarrassed. 'I'd rather not say,' she said.

'But you have to say,' he said.

'It was you.'

'No it wasn't!'

'Yes it was.'

''Twasn't.'

'"Twas.'

'I've never said bollocks in public in my life!'

'You have. You just said it.'

'That doesn't count.'

'Anyway you said it.'

'When am I supposed to have said it?'

'Two weekends ago. On a Saturday afternoon.'

The acting chairman thought for a while. We all waited. This was too good for anyone to interrupt. 'I missed a two footer and lost £10,' he admitted. 'I might have been feeling peeved about that.' He nodded wisely. 'I may well have expressed my unhappiness,' he admitted.

'You were betting?' cried the woman in pink, a vision of outrage. 'And you lost £10?' Her voice rose and she sounded like a provincial actress over-playing the part of Lady Bracknell in *The Importance Of Being Ernest.*

'If I hadn't missed that short putt I wouldn't have lost £10,' explained her husband. 'That was why I said 'bollocks'.'

'You were betting and then you swore!' said the woman in pink, who clearly could not have been more shocked if she had suddenly discovered that her husband was a white slave trader.

'Well what do you want me to do about it?' demanded her husband.

'My fellow lady members and I have discussed this and we want all bad language to be outlawed,' said the woman in pink. 'It's the only solution. 'Any male member heard swearing must be given disciplinary points and suspended from the club for a month. Any player who receives three suspensions will be expelled from the club. It'll be like speeding. We have formed a Standards Supervisory Sub-Committee to police this new regulation.'

'What new regulation?'

'The no swearing regulation.'

'It isn't a regulation yet.'

'Well, we want it to be.'

'We have to vote on it first,' said the acting chairman. He waved a hand around to indicate that there were other people present. 'And I have to see what other members think about it.'

'Well see what other members think about it,' said the woman in pink, the acting chairman's wife. 'Have a vote. And then we'll have our new regulation. And if you say the word again you'll be punished.'

A stout, bald man in a blue jumper struggled to his feet. He looked to be too big to be standing up without support. 'I think this new regulation is bloody stupid,' he said, to great laughter and some scattered applause. 'Civilisation has been going steadily downhill since women got the vote. If we give in to this we might as well just give up completely.' He collapsed back into his chair and the canvas groaned.

A man in a green tweed jacket spoke without standing. 'We have to be firm on this,' he said. 'Women are wonderful creatures but they can occasionally be judgmental, narrow-minded and unfair.' There were murmurs of protest from the few women present. Someone threw a powder puff which missed him. 'It's true,' insisted the man. 'My wife and I only ever argue when she is being unreasonable.' He sat down. The woman in pink and her colleagues opened and shut their mouths like goldfish. The woman who had thrown the powder puff sent a message across the room asking if she could please have her powder puff back.

'Since the ladies are so sensitive I think we should find some other way to protect them,' said a man with large ears and strands of hair combed over a bald pate.

'What do you suggest?' asked the acting chairman. He seemed to have gained strength and confidence from the support of other male members.

'We could ban the serving of food and drinks on the terrace,' the man with large ears suggested.

'Oh no, that's going too far,' said the acting chairman, shaking his head. 'Sitting on the terrace with a nice G&T is a pleasant way to round off an evening.'

'We could move the terrace to the other side of the clubhouse,' suggested someone else.

'And overlook the rubbish bins and the car park?' The acting chairman snorted with disapproval. 'I don't think so.'

'Mr Acting Chairman,' said Oliver, standing up, 'I have a suggestion.'

'What's that?'

'Ban ladies from the terrace,' suggested Oliver. 'Then their delicate feelings won't be outraged by hearing bad language from nasty male players who lose £10 in skins matches.'

The acting chairman thought about this for a moment and slowly a smile appeared on his face. 'That seems like a very good solution,' he agreed.

'Don't you dare!' threatened his wife. 'If you do I'll...'

'You'll what?' interrupted her husband, whose new courage was growing by the minute. 'I can get my shirts ironed at the Chinese laundry. I can get my meals here. What other services are you going to withdraw?'

The woman in pink went an even brighter shade of red but said nothing.

'Let's take a vote,' said the acting chairman. 'All those in favour of banning lady members from the terrace?'

Every man in the room put up a hand. Some put up two.

'Anyone against?'

The woman in pink, and the other half a dozen women present, put up a hand each.

'Motion carried by a substantial margin,' announced the acting chairman. 'You may as well call it unanimous,' he added, speaking to the club secretary who was keeping the minutes.

The acting chairman's wife stood up, adjusted her hat, and headed for the door. When she got there she hesitated for a moment. Everyone in the room was watching her and waiting to see what she would say. Her husband held his head high and did not waiver. 'Don't be too late back,' said the acting chairman's wife rather meekly. 'You know how I worry if you get home late.'

'I'll be back when I'm ready, dear,' boomed the acting chairman.

'Yes, dear,' said his wife. 'Would you like your usual cocoa when you get in?'

'I'll let you know what I want when I get home,' said the acting chairman.

'Yes, dear,' said his wife. She left, followed by most of the other lady members.

Gerald stood up. 'Gentlemen,' he said. 'I suggest that we now close the meeting and all buy the acting chairman a drink.'

This suggestion was greeted with loud cheering. The acting chairman, who had never been so popular nor felt so proud of himself, grew visibly larger. The meeting broke up.

'Nothing seems to have been decided,' I said to Simon, as we stood.

'Oh, I don't know about that,' said Simon. 'The acting chairman has established his authority at home and lots of niggles have been aired. That seems to me like a pretty good evening's work.'

A red-faced man in a brown suit appeared in the doorway. It was the club chairman. 'I'm here now,' he announced loudly and rather pompously. 'We can start the meeting.'

But no one took any notice of him. We were all busy queuing up to buy drinks for the acting chairman.

Chapter Eighteen
'Just The Right Amount Of Mud.'

The four of us were sitting in our corner by the fire, having a round of drinks before a round of golf. Outside, it was cold; bitterly, finger-freezing cold. Tucked snugly in the lounge bar we were fortifying ourselves with spirits. Gerald and Oliver were drinking brandy. Simon and I were drinking malt whisky.

'I read somewhere that it is dangerous to go outside in the cold after drinking alcohol,' said Gerald.

'Is that so?' said Simon, thoughtfully. He sniffed and then sipped at his whisky.

'It's started to rain,' said Oliver, who was the only one of us sitting in a position from which he could clearly see what was happening outside; he had a clear view through the lounge bar windows which overlook both the 18th green and the practice green. 'The sky is black and getting blacker by the minute.'

'It'll probably thunder,' said Simon. 'The fellow on the radio said that there would be storms.'

'I wonder if it's perhaps too dangerous to go out and play,' said Gerald. 'The ground is icy. A storm is brewing. Lightning coming. And we've all been drinking spirits.' He raised an eyebrow quizzically.

'If we were all single men like Tom I wouldn't worry,' said Oliver. 'But..,' and he sighed, 'I do have family responsibilities.'

'I'm no fair weather golfer,' said Simon.

'Absolutely not!' agreed Gerald immediately.

'I've played many a game of golf in bad weather.'

'We all have.'

'But on a day like this, and thinking of our responsibilities, it's probably better to stay indoors,' said Simon, as though unwillingly but nobly accepting the sacrifice. 'We have to think of our families.'

'If we're staying in I'll just pop and ask Elvis to take my gear out and get it muddy,' said Oliver. He yawned, stretched, got up and walked over to the bar where he tapped a youth of about twenty on the shoulder and started talking to him.

'What on earth is Oliver doing?' I asked Simon. 'Who is Elvis?'

'Elvis is one of the juniors. Oliver has gone to get him to play nine holes in his clothes and with his clubs,' said Simon.

I stared at Simon. I didn't understand.

'He and Elvis are about the same size,' explained Simon.

'I can see that,' I said, watching as the two men left the room together.

'If Oliver's wife finds out he's been here sitting by the fire drinking she'll go mad,' said Simon. 'She's given him standing instructions that if he comes here to play golf and the weather is too bad then he's to go back home and do something useful.'

'What sort of useful?'

'Oh I dunno, put up a shelf in the bathroom or clear out the garage.'

'Oh, that sort of useful.'

'Exactly. So Oliver gives Elvis a few bob to play a few holes in his shoes and his clothes, using his clubs.'

'So that when Oliver gets home it looks as if he's been playing golf? Muddy shoes, muddy clubs, soggy glove? Just the right amount of mud on the bottom of his trousers?'

'Precisely,' nodded Simon. 'He did try faking it but it didn't work. It's difficult to get it just right. Too easy to over do it. You can never get the mud splashes just right without actually going out there and splashing in the mud. If you have to go to all that effort yourself you might just as well go and play golf.'

'I'll get another round of drinks,' said Gerald. 'Doubles everyone?'

'Triples would save us getting up and moving about so much,' said Simon.

'Splendid idea,' said Gerald, heading off towards the bar.

* * *

'Thinking of thunder and lightning reminds me of old Lightning,' said Simon.

'Ah,' said Oliver, who had returned. He had given his clothes to Elvis and was now wearing a spare pair of light green slacks and a mauve jumper which he had taken from his locker. 'I remember Lightning!'

'Who on earth was Lightning?' I asked.

Simon settled comfortably into his chair. 'Odd bloke. Mad keen on golf and born to the game. Tiny little golf balls instead of blood corpuscles. It was rumoured that he had been conceived in a bunker just to the left of the 14th green and it was an undeniable fact that he had been delivered on the 17th tee by two dermatologists, an orthopaedic surgeon and a psychiatrist who were, fortuitously, taking part in the annual medical society golf day.'

'His parents and godparents were all low handicappers,' said Oliver. 'His father was a surgeon of some kind. His parents were quite well off but Lightning was the meanest man I've ever met. I remember that when they went shopping he and his wife used to stay in the car park until their ticket expired because he wanted to make sure he got his money's worth. He would take the newspaper with him and his wife would make up a packet of sandwiches. They'd sit there until their time had expired and then go home.'

'He was a very slow player,' said Simon.

'Hence the soubriquet Lightning,' explained Oliver. 'He would often take eight or nine hours to play one round of golf. His record, I think, was over eleven hours.'

'Generally speaking, slower even than the four horsewomen of the Apocalypse,' said Simon. He looked at Oliver. 'Tell him the story about Lightning,' he said.

'You tell him,' said Oliver. 'You were there when it happened. I was at my sister's wedding.' He wrinkled his brow and thought for a moment. 'Her third I think it was. Might have been her fourth.'

'Lightning wasn't all that bad a player,' began Simon. 'But he was a hooker and a slicer. Nothing worse for a golfer than being a hooker and a slicer. You don't know where the ball is going. If you hook and you know you're going to hook you can make allowances. A hook you can rely on really isn't all that much of a problem. Ditto with slicing. But if you don't know whether the ball is going to go right or left you're sunk really, aren't you?'

I nodded.

'Lightning never had the faintest where his drive was going to end up. He'd hook and slice all over the place. One minute his ball would fly left. And the next shot would veer right. His speciality was the late swerve. I've never seen anyone swerve the ball quite so late. Down the fairway it would fly. He and his partners would think it was going straight down the middle. People would congratulate him. And then, just as the ball began to lose height so the swerve would begin.' Simon shook his head at the memory of Lightning's late swerving drives.

'Now, none of this would have mattered all that much if Lightning had not been so mean,' continued Simon. 'He was, without a shadow of a doubt, the meanest man I've ever met in my entire life. And I know about mean. When I was a lad, my best friend's dad was a farmer. He was pretty mean. He never gave his children anything to eat except porridge because they all hated the sight of it and so a packet lasted quite a long time. I went there once for tea. The farmer argued that if he only gave them food they didn't like they'd never get fat and he said he was really being much kinder than parents who gave their kids buns, jelly, ice cream and chocolate cake. Of course, neither my pal nor any of the other children were convinced by this because they knew that in reality their father was just a mean old man. Sometimes on a Saturday night he would give all the children sixpence if they agreed to go to bed without any supper. Then, if they bought into this, he'd get it back the next morning by charging them sixpence for their breakfast.'

Oliver said that his father had been a farmer and that all this was very unfair to farmers and he insisted that farmers got a very poor press from people who really ought to know better. He said that when he was a boy he once heard of someone who knew of a farmer who let all the local children go onto his land and pick up dead branches and twigs and take them away to burn on bonfire night. He never charged them a penny, said Oliver. Simon agreed that this was very generous of the unknown farmer and solemn proof that we all ought to be much more careful about telling nasty stories about farmers in the future.

'Anyway,' continued Simon, 'to get back to Lightning. He was far meaner than my pal's father, the farmer.' He emptied his glass and looked over towards the bar. 'What on earth is Gerald doing?' he asked.

'Flirting with the bar staff,' said Oliver, nodding in Gerald's direction. Gerald was smiling and talking to a very pretty girl behind the bar. There was no one else there. 'You watch,' said Oliver, 'Gerald will claim there was a terrible crush when he gets back.'

'You know the gorse bushes both sides of the third hole?' said Simon.

'Very well,' I admitted, ruefully. I had lost a fair number of balls in those bushes.

'Lightning's drive on the third would always go straight into the gorse,' continued Simon. Whatever club he took off the tee his ball would fly unerringly into the gorse. Left or right it didn't matter. There was no escape. I actually used to feel sorry for him sometimes.'

'Now, as you know, many players don't even bother to look for balls when they go into the gorse. It's horribly thick stuff. But Lightning would take a pair of gardening gloves out of his crumbling leather golf bag and wade into the gorse with steady determination. He had four different types of ball-retriever in his bag – two for fishing balls out of water, one for rescuing balls from thick gorse and a fourth for picking balls out of trees. One of his ball retrievers had an extension specially built for him by a local blacksmith. He could rescue balls from the middle of Loch Ness with it. Some of us believed he played golf because he liked finding golf balls. Thirty or forty minutes after striding into the gorse, having filled his pockets with the balls other players had lost and abandoned, Lightning would give a little whoop of delight when he finally came across the ball he had originally lost. The most doting parent would not have spent as much time looking for a missing child as Lightning spent looking for a missing ball. His partners, who were invariably press-ganged into taking part in the search, would stumble back onto the course, scratched and bleeding, muttering incantations to their gods to keep Lightning's next shot on the fairway. But, sadly, the gods never seemed to pay a great deal of attention.'

'On an average sort of day it would take Lightning half an hour to play each hole. Most of that time he would spend in the undergrowth. He was the best finder of golf balls I ever met. Better even than that dog one of the groundsmen used to have.'

'Sally.'

'That was her name. Amazing dog. But not as good at finding balls as Lightning. Each time he waded into the rough he would find ten or fifteen golf balls. All previously abandoned as lost by other players.'

'He found clubs too,' said Oliver.

'I remember,' said Simon. 'Golfers would throw clubs into the undergrowth in disgust and Lightning would fish them out.'

'And there was a naked body wasn't there?'

'There was,' agreed Simon. 'He once found the dead and decaying body of an unfortunate woman who had, it turned out, been missing from home for several weeks.'

Nobody said anything for a while as we sat in silent tribute to this unknown cadaver.

Eventually Simon broke the silence and carried on with his story.

'If Lightning was proud of the fact that he never paid for his golf balls,' he said, 'he was equally proud of the fact that he would use the same ball for months and months until the casing literally flew apart. A fellow who used to play with him occasionally said that Lightning once played with a ball in such poor condition that a shot sent the casing and the core in different directions. Naturally, Lightning wasn't satisfied until he had found both halves. I don't know which half he played.'

I was sceptical about this claim, arguing that no one could possibly be so mean. But Simon insisted that he wasn't exaggerating at all. He swore that he had often watched Lightning collecting together broken golf tees and that he had once spotted him in the changing room gluing them back together again. Simon said he didn't think he had ever seen anyone mending broken tees before and that for a while he'd amused himself by collecting together broken bits and pieces and giving them to Lightning to repair. He says, however, that he gave this up when Lightning tried to sell him back the reconditioned tees at a special price. He said what really worried him was the fact that he had been tempted by Lightning's offer.

'Eventually,' continued Simon, 'it became a favourite club pastime to try and bait poor Lightning. One of the most popular games was to try to get Lightning to pay for a round of drinks. People would sidle up to him in the bar, buy him a drink and then stand around fingering their empty glass for hours afterwards, waiting for the compliment to be returned. They always waited in vain for Lightning never opened his wallet in anger.'

'I remember we used to take bets on who might be able to get him to buy a drink,' said Oliver. 'We gave it up after three months. He hadn't bought anyone a drink and there didn't seem any likelihood that he ever would. The odds had become absurdly long. I think that by the time we finished we were offering at least 500 to 1 against him buying a drink.'

'In the end,' said Simon, 'it took the combined efforts of just about everyone in the club to squeeze drinks out of Lightning and the way they did this was, I think, a tribute to our combined ingenuity and imagination.'

'It must have been brilliant,' said Oliver. 'I've never forgiven my sister for getting married that day. I don't expect it lasted. Her marriages never do.'

'You will recall,' Simon said to me, 'that the green on the second short hole is partly hidden from the view of the player both when he is on the tee and for about fifty yards of the walk down the fairway.'

I nodded.

'Well, one summer Sunday lunchtime, the woodlands around this hole were alive with crouching club members. Every tee and bush hid at least a foursome. The whole operation was run like a military operation.'

'After Lightning had hit his tee shot one member ran out and picked his ball from the bushes where it had landed. He then threw the ball to a second member crouched on the green right by the flagpost. This second member then dropped the ball into the hole and ran off the green back into the undergrowth.'

'In order to make sure that Lightning was distracted and confused his playing partner – the club's assistant professional who had, much to Lightning's surprise and delight, agreed to play a round with him – had 'accidentally' collided with him the moment he had played his shot. This prevented Lightning from following the flight of his ball with his usual care. The result of this, combined with the peculiar geography of the hole, was that Lightning had no idea where his ball had gone.'

"Don't worry about it,' the assistant professional said, after apologising profusely, 'I saw your ball land on the green. Lovely shot. Well played.' The professional had already played and his ball had run off the back of the green into a bunker. They then set off down the fairway.'

'When they got near to the green Lightning looked disappointed at not being able to see his ball on the putting surface but began to walk round and round in ever decreasing circles, searching the bunkers and poking around in the light rough around the green.'

'It was the professional, Lightning's playing partner, who eventually came across the ball. He feigned surprise and delight and called Lightning across to look at the ball which was, surprise surprise, lying in the bottom of the cup.'

"Is that your ball?" the professional asked.'

Lightning bent down, picked up the ball and identified it as his.

"A hole in one!' cried the assistant professional excitedly. 'You've got a hole in one! Congratulations!' He leant over, checked the ball and confirmed that it was, indeed, the ball Lightning had been playing. Naturally, Lightning beamed with delight.'

'The story now moves on a few hours. It is early afternoon. Lightning is finishing his round of golf. It has been uneventful except for that single hole in one. As Lightning approaches the clubhouse he hears applause. He looks up and sees a cluster of members standing on the putting green, clapping. He asks what they are clapping. They tell him that they are clapping him. They have somehow found out about his hole in one. They are thrilled for him. As Lightning walks towards the clubhouse so the crowd grows bigger. Soon there are nearly a hundred members gathered around him. They lead him into the lounge. He tells them that he is worried because he is still wearing his spiked shoes but they tell him not to worry. Lightning is confused. Part of him is delighted and proud to share this exciting and memorable occasion with so many enthusiastic fellow members. But part of him is puzzled and wary.'

'Lightning's wariness is justified for as soon as they have all congratulated him on the hole in one members start calling out their drinks orders to the bar staff. Lightning knows as well as anyone that a player who scores a hole in one has to buy everyone in the clubhouse a drink. Pleased as he is with his success he would have preferred to keep his accomplishment secret.'

"I haven't got any money on me,' he murmurs desperately.'

"No problem," promises the assistant professional. 'In circumstances like this the club will just send you a bill.' Lightning opens and shuts his mouth but nothing comes out.'

'Just about every member in the club is there. It is the busiest Sunday lunchtime anyone can ever remember seeing. Members order double brandies, double malt whiskies and treble pink gins.'

Simon said the total bill came to several hundred pounds and that it was a shock Lightning never came to terms with.

'He resigned from the club a week or two afterwards,' said Simon, 'and was never seen there again, except for one or two occasions when he came by to try to sell golf balls. One or two members who were approached said that his car boot was crammed with cardboard boxes full of balls and reconditioned tees. Someone said later that they had seen him playing on a municipal course nearby but that he had refused to play the two short holes there.'

'Is he still alive?' I asked.

'Died a couple of years ago,' said Simon. 'When he died the secretary got a letter from Lightning's solicitor asking if it would be all right with us if his widow scattered his ashes in the gorse bushes. The solicitor said Lightning wanted to be laid to rest there because that was where he'd spent some of his happiest hours. Naturally, the club agreed. There was a little ceremony I remember. Quite moving.'

'Sorry about the delay,' said Gerald, arriving back with a tray of drinks. 'There was a huge crush at the bar. Chap in front of me must have been ordering drinks for his regiment.'

'Ah there's Elvis,' said Oliver, nodding towards the door where the youngster stood, soaked, bedraggled and mud spattered. Oliver levered himself to his feet and sauntered over to congratulate the youngster on his good work. As he did so he took out his wallet and removed what looked like a £20 note.

It seemed a reasonable price to pay for not having to clear out the garage.

Chapter Nineteen

'The Man Who Thought He Was A Golfer.'

'I've heard about a wonderful new way to cure a slice,' said Gerald, one Saturday evening. We were enjoying a game of playing-card golf and he cursed as the five of hearts teetered on the edge of Simon's fedora, looked as though it was going to hold and then fell to the carpet. 'It was in one of the golf magazines. This American chap says it's possible to get rid of a slice using something he calls 'mental imagery'. Apparently you don't even need to go out onto the practice green to perfect it. You can do all your practice in the bar, or sitting in front of the fire. The chap says he's got clients who had never previously hit the same ball twice who now drive every ball as straight as an arrow.'

With a skilful, practised flick of the wrist Simon sent the queen of spades spinning right into the centre of his own fedora.
'Good shot!' said Oliver, admiringly. 'That's your hole. What's the score?'

'My game. Six and five,' said Simon. 'You lot need to get in some more practice.' He picked up his fedora and took out four £10 notes and a small number of playing cards. I got up and helped him pick up the other cards, scattered across the carpet in the approximate neighbourhood.

Gerald, ignoring all this activity, said that the writer of the article he'd read had claimed that all the golfer has to do is to close his eyes before playing a shot and to imagine that he can see the ball flying directly towards the target he's aiming at. He said the writer claimed that if he did this the golfer would have extra confidence, his muscles would work properly and he'd play like a different man. Gerald said he fully intended to try it out himself as soon as he had a free moment or two in which to practise but he said it wasn't something he needed urgently since he wasn't as desperately unhappy about his game as he felt sure the rest of us must be.

I listened to Gerald very carefully. He reads a lot of golfing instructional books and tears out and files the advice pages from the various golfing publications to which he subscribes.

'I wouldn't try it, if I were you,' warned Simon. 'A fellow I knew quite well tried that technique once and it ruined his life. It was at a club where I used to play when I was young. Amazing story.'

'I'll get the drinks,' said Gerald. 'I don't want to miss this. Talk about the weather until I get back.'

We talked about the weather for a few minutes while Gerald made the expedition to the bar and back again.

'Right,' said Gerald, settling down in his chair and unwrapping the large cigar he had bought. 'Now tell me why we shouldn't try this mental imagery stuff.'

'The chap I knew wasn't a bad golfer,' began Simon, 'but he had a couple of nasty little habits that annoyed him out of all proportion. When hitting long irons off the fairway he quite often topped the ball and sent it skidding and scuttling along the grass for twenty or thirty yards. And when getting out of sand he frequently managed to bury the ball even deeper.'

We all nodded sagely. These were faults with which we were all too familiar. (Mind you, to be fair, I don't suppose there are any golf faults with which we are not familiar.)

'Lessons from the golf professional didn't help,' said Simon. 'And then one day he found an American book describing this mental imagery technique. It was called something else then, I think, but it was the same stuff. He used to sit in his bedroom imagining really good golf shots. Then, when he got out onto the course, he would, before playing a shot, imagine the ball going exactly where he wanted it to go.'

'That's the stuff,' said Gerald, excitedly. 'That's what I was reading about.'

'To his immense surprise it worked,' said Simon. 'In the short-term it was marvellous. But in the long-term it was probably the worst thing that could have happened to him.'

'Why?' demanded Gerald. 'What on earth happened?'

'I'm coming to that,' said Simon, holding up a hand. 'Just be patient. Since this chap was getting such good results by imagining his long iron and bunker shots he decided to try using the same trick on all his golf shots. It meant that a round of golf took him seven or eight hours to complete but it halved his handicap in weeks. The slowness in itself wasn't an insuperable problem because the golf professional who made up the foursomes for Sunday morning matches just put him with a trio of octogenarians whose arthritis ensured that they took that long anyway.'

'Things went on like this for a couple of months,' continued Simon, 'and then suddenly this chap stopped going out on the course at all. He came to the club as he had always done but he just sat in the bar with his eyes closed quite tightly. He used to keep a drink in his hand so that he didn't have to open them to find it again, and he'd give the barman standing instructions to keep it topped up. When we asked him why he wasn't playing any more he said it was because he got just as much pleasure from playing an imaginary round as he did from playing a real round. He said it was quicker and he hadn't lost a ball for ages and that he never got wet however much it rained. He even filled a score card at the end of his imaginary rounds and handed it to the club secretary.'

'After a month or two of this he claimed his handicap ought to be brought down to scratch since he hadn't played a single bad shot in that time. He got very upset when people laughed at this and soon after that he stopped coming to the club at all. He used to stay at home, sit in his living room and play his rounds of golf there in front of the fire. He even fixed up a little contraption with a gin bottle and a piece of rubber tubing so that he could keep his glass filled even though his eyes were closed.'

'After that things went from unusual to eccentric and straight on to stark raving crazy in a very short space of time. I managed to put the story together afterwards after talking to friends and one or two other club members but it seems that after a few weeks of sitting in the living room playing golf he'd given up going downstairs at all and had started playing golf in bed. When his wife, a sweet, gentle long suffering creature who had a lovely touch with crochet needles and a rare talent for making woolly club covers, remonstrated with him he told her that he didn't see any point in going downstairs when he could do everything so much better by just lying still, closing his eyes and using his mental imagery technique.'

'When he eventually stopped eating and drinking because he said he could imagine all sorts of delicious foods and thirst-quenching drinks his wife got worried and called the doctor. There was the most awful row and the doctor ended up by saying that this chap would have to go into hospital.' 'Naturally the poor fellow insisted that he could quite easily imagine himself going into hospital and so what was the point in actually taking him there?'

Simon said that they took him away in a strait-jacket though they had to sedate him first. The men in white coats arrived and carried him very discreetly into a waiting ambulance.

'I still hear from his wife every Christmas,' said Simon. 'She sends me a card to let me know how they are getting on and often encloses a crocheted club cover too. The last time I heard her husband was still being force-fed but was regularly going round in fifty five.'

When Simon had finished his story we sat in silence for a few moments.

'Makes you think, doesn't it?' said Oliver faintly.

'I'm glad I didn't try it now,' said Gerald, wiping his brow with a plum coloured handkerchief. 'I'll put the article in the shredder when I get back home.'

'I'll get the drinks,' I offered.

I felt as though we had all just survived a very close call.

Chapter Twenty
'The Record Holder.'

The club's annual Long Hitting Competition had been held and the talk in the lounge bar was about little else.

Naturally, the losers (of whom there were a good number) all had good excuses and were able to put forward excellent reasons why they should have won. They were enjoying an orgy of protesting and explaining.

The winner (of whom there was only one) was simply enjoying his moment. Not having to think up excuses he could concentrate on smiling and buying drinks for people.

Oliver, Gerald, Simon and I were, as usual, sitting near to the fire. Not having taken part in the main competition (none of us were self-deluded enough to think we could possibly win) we were able to assess the competition with some objectivity.

'How far did the winner hit his ball?' asked Oliver.

'I think it was just over 320 yards,' replied Gerald.

'321 yards,' said Simon. 'It's a new club record.'

'A good hit,' said Oliver. 'Though I have it on good authority that his ball hit a stone on the fairway and had a lucky bounce forwards.'

'Who said that?' demanded Gerald.

'I can't say,' said Oliver. 'I was sworn to secrecy.'

'Who was it?' persisted Gerald.

'It would be a betrayal for me to reveal his name,' insisted Oliver.

'Go on,' said Gerald. 'Tell us and I'll buy you a packet of pork scratchings.'

'The chap who came second,' replied Oliver, instantly.

'I bet the head greenkeeper didn't like that,' said Gerald.

'He said there are no stones on his golf course,' said Oliver. 'Not even in the rough.'

We all smiled and nodded. It was just the sort of thing the head greenkeeper would say.

'But I once hit a drive which went much further than that,' said Oliver.

I looked at him, surprised. 'I didn't even know you'd ever entered,' I said.

'Oh, not in a long driving competition,' said Oliver. 'But my ball went a lot further than 321 yards.'

'Tell him the story,' said Gerald, standing up. 'I've heard this one so I'll go and get in another round of drinks while I'm getting Oliver's pork scratchings. There's quite a scrum at the bar so it could take me some time.'

'I'll give you a hand,' offered Simon who had clearly also heard Oliver's story. The two of them departed.

* * *

'My ball went just over seven miles,' began Oliver. 'Seven and a quarter miles we estimated later.'

'You hit a ball which went seven miles?' I said, incredulously.

'Absolutely,' nodded Oliver. He smiled at my obvious bemusement. 'Scout's honour.'

I thought about this for a few moments, quite unable to think of an explanation. 'Was it winter?' I asked. 'Was the ground frozen over? Icy?'

'No, not at all,' said Oliver. 'It was mid-summer. I was playing in shorts and a short-sleeved shirt. My partners were two guys called Fame and Fortune. They changed their names by deed poll and ran a talent agency.'

'And it was here? On this course?'

Oliver nodded.

'To liven things up a little we were playing a game we used to play quite often in those days. We were playing to see how far round the course we could get with just one ball. The rules were simple: if you sent your ball out of bounds you still had to play it;

if it landed in water or nettles you had to play it as it lay. If, for whatever reason, you didn't play the ball you'd started with you lost the match. All laws which might interfere with this simple rule were temporarily suspended.'

'Sounds a pretty good idea,' I agreed.

'Harder than you might think,' said Oliver.

'Did you hit your ball over the hedge? Onto the road?' I asked. 'I suppose if a ball just bounced along the road it might travel quite a distance.'

'Close,' confirmed Oliver. 'I did hit my ball over the hedge. But it didn't just bounce along the road. In fact, it didn't hit the road at all.'

'A car?' I suggested. 'You hit your ball into a car?'

'Lorry, actually,' said Oliver with a broad grin. 'I hit my drive into the back of a builder's lorry. When my drive veered left over the hedge – I was hooking a lot more in those days – I naturally just thought I'd lost the ball, the match and the £25 we were playing for. But the lorry was full of sand and to my absolute astonishment I could see my ball sitting up quite nicely on top of the pile of sand. It looked very playable. The odds against my ball landing in the back of a lorry must have been at least a million to one. The chances of it staying there and not bouncing out must have been fairly considerable too. But that is exactly what happened.' He took out a small cigar, and played with it for a moment, examining it from every angle before lighting it. 'If I'd been playing an ordinary match, under ordinary rules, I would have just waved the ball goodbye and played three off the tee. But the ball wasn't lost at all. I knew exactly where it was. It looked perfectly playable. And if I could just play it back onto the course I would, I thought, still have a chance of winning.'

'So you chased after the lorry?'

'I grabbed a wedge from my bag, told my partners to wait for me, wriggled through the hedge and chased off after the lorry.'

'And you chased it for seven miles?'

'I borrowed a bicycle parked outside the supermarket,' admitted Oliver. 'Fortunately, there was a lot of traffic so the lorry couldn't get up much speed. Eventually, I caught up with the driver at a set of traffic lights right in the middle of town. I pedalled up alongside the cab. Since it was a nice warm day, the driver had his window open. Rather breathless by then I managed to explain what had happened and asked if he could stop for a moment so that I could play my ball out of the sand in the back of his lorry. As luck would have it, he wasn't a golfer himself but he did enjoy watching golf on the television and he didn't mind helping. He pulled over to the side of the road as soon as he'd gone through the traffic lights and helped me climb up into the back of the lorry. By this time, of course, quite a crowd had gathered around to watch this lunatic about to play a bunker shot out of the back of a builder's lorry.'

'You managed to play it out?'

'Even if I do say so myself, I played a very nice little chip shot out of the sand and onto a tiny piece of grass in front of a drinking fountain and two benches.' Oliver emptied his glass and took several long, slow puffs at his cigar before resuming his story.

'It was at this point that the policeman turned up,' he continued. 'I was just working out how best to play back to the golf course, and had pretty much decided that the only thing I could do was to just try and scoot the ball along the gutter, when I felt someone tap me on my shoulder. At first I thought it was just another golfer offering advice – I'd already had at least half a dozen people offer their thoughts on the most appropriate sort of shot to play – but it was a policeman. Nice chap. Didn't play golf, though. He told me point blank that if I tried hitting a golf ball down a busy road he'd arrest me. He didn't say what for but he said he was pretty confident he'd think of something.'

'Crumbs.'

'It was at that point,' Oliver went on, 'that I had a bit of a brainwave. The bicycle I had borrowed was fitted with two large panniers so I lay it down on the grass right next to the ball and opened up the lower of the two panniers. With the policeman's permission I gently tapped the ball into the open pannier. Then I stood the bicycle upright, waved goodbye to the lorry driver, who was by this time having quite an argument with a traffic warden, and pedalled back to the golf course. When I got there I tipped the bike on its side so that the ball rolled out. I then played my ball back over the hedge, put the bicycle back where I'd found it, slipped through the hedge and carried on playing.'

'Were your two playing partners waiting for you?'

'Yes, they were. They were lying on the grass having a quiet smoke. They had, they told me, waved through nineteen pairs and twelve foursomes. There was a bloke playing by himself but they wouldn't let him through. As you know, singletons have no precedence at all; they are rather like the third sons of Earls – everyone ignores them. This poor chap had made a daisy chain seventeen feet long by the time we were ready to carry on.'

'Did you win?'

'Sadly, no. Four shots later I put my ball straight into a deep pond. I waded in up to my waist but it was hopeless. The ball was gone. It's probably still there.'

'So how do you know how far your ball travelled?'

'I measured the distance in the car two days later,' said Oliver. 'Just over seven miles. Longest golf shot ever hit. We've often thought of trying to break my seven mile record. But when you do it knowingly it sort of takes the fun out of it. There wouldn't be any element of excitement. You could just chip into the back of a lorry heading north and then chip out again five hundred miles later. Or you could chip into a railway carriage in Plymouth and chip out in Edinburgh.' He pulled a face. 'No challenge,' he said. 'What sort of a golf shot would that be?'

Five minutes later Gerald and Simon arrived back with the drinks.

'Even the winner of this year's competition is now moaning,' said Simon.

'He claims that if his ball hadn't hit one of those white marker posts they put along the side of the fairway it would have gone another twenty yards,' said Gerald.

'Don't know why he's bothering,' said Oliver, accepting his packet of pork scratchings from Gerald. '321 yards, 341 yards – what does it matter?' He shrugged the shrug of a quietly confident man. It would, he knew, be a long time before anyone broke *his* long driving record.

Chapter Twenty One
'Bad Golfers Have More Fun.'

'Happy birthday!' said Simon as we met in the locker room. 'As a special treat I've hired you a caddy for the afternoon.'

'A real caddy?' I enquired.

'A real caddy,' nodded Simon. 'Actually I've hired two. One each. Gnarled, weather-beaten fellows with no teeth and backs made of oak; chaps who look somehow unfinished when they walk without a bag over their shoulder; chaps who always know what club you should use.'

'Caddies?' I said, startled. 'Do we need them?'

Simon put a hand on my shoulder and looked at me carefully. 'I don't know if I've ever told you this,' he confided. 'But in my heart I've long believed that I could beat any of the pros on the big tours if only I had their advantages. It would really be much fairer if we all played with the same clubs and the same balls. If I had the advantages they have I could play like any of them. Those guys have nothing but the best and I'm still struggling around with last year's ironmongery.' He paused for a moment, gathering his thoughts. 'Did you know that the professionals have an endless supply of free balls?'

I admitted that I did not know this.

'Box fulls, armfuls, lorry loads,' he said. 'All brand new. They must spend half their lives unwrapping golf balls.' He thought about this, as did I. 'Though actually of course,' he said, 'they would just get their caddies to do that for them, wouldn't they?'

He paused again and stared dreamily into space. 'The best clubs, beautifully manicured fairways, a psychologist on tap to help them over the bad moments and,' he paused yet again, this time for effect, 'they have caddies.'

'Caddies.'

'A good caddy has got to be worth ten or fifteen shots a round,' said Simon. 'You've seen these superstar players on the television. Who is it who picks out the club for the top guys when they're stuck in the rough? The caddy, of course. Who is it bending down reading the line of that long, snaking putt? The caddy.'

'Where on earth did you find two real caddies?' I asked him.

'Through a chap who buys envelopes from my shop,' said Simon. 'He rang up someone he knows and got a phone number.'

'These are caddies who caddy for professionals?'

'Absolutely. Professionals and celebrities. They're probably on first name terms with Jack Nicklaus, Arnold Palmer and Jimmy Tarbuck. Some of these chaps are real characters, you know. I once hired a caddy when I played in Scotland.'

'Royal and Ancient?' I asked.

'I don't think he was royal but he was certainly ancient,' said Simon. He'd had his teeth knocked out by a rather wild American golfer and had had them wired. The result was that he couldn't talk. He didn't say a single word all afternoon; he just spat into the gorse every time I hit the ball. I hit the ball a lot so he did a lot of spitting.'

'He doesn't sound as if he was a great deal of help,' I protested.

'He wasn't,' agreed Simon. 'He was a rogue. I should have guessed there was something iffy about him when he insisted on meeting me on the second tee. I had to carry my own clubs up the first. But don't worry, the two chaps I've hired for us are proper professionals.'

'But I've never played with a caddy!' I protested. 'I wouldn't know what you have to do.' I thought about it for a moment. 'Do you have to ask for advice? Do you listen? Won't they expect us to hit four hundred yards from the tee with a nine iron and then pitch up onto the green within a foot of the pin?'

'All you have to do is tip them a quid at the end of the round,' insisted Simon. 'They'll love you for life and their grandchildren will still be sending your grandchildren Christmas cards long after you've lost your last ball.'

'Right,' I said. 'You think a quid will be enough?' I knew that Simon wasn't always entirely worldly. I had seen him give the bar steward a five pence piece for fetching his waterproofs from his car.

'These chaps don't live like you and I,' said Simon. 'They are men of nature; they live rough. They live in tiny little wooden huts hidden away behind the trees on the 14th at Muirfield.'

'Are there trees on the 14th at Muirfield?'

'I don't have the faintest idea. It was one of those what do you call thems. A figure of speech?'

'Oh.'

'Poetic licence.'

'Ah.'

'Perhaps they may one day aspire to caravans parked on a bit of scrap land behind the driving range,' continued Simon. He thought for a moment or two. 'Maybe a couple of quid then,' he conceded. 'They still have to buy bread and milk I guess. But a couple of quid will keep them in the necessities for their simple lifestyles for weeks. Give one of these guys a Guinness and a cheese sandwich and he's yours for life.'

'You don't do the shopping do you?' I said.

'Of course not,' said Simon. 'Why on earth would I want to do the shopping?' He shrugged aside this apparent non sequitur.

* * *

'I've never understood why people look for lost balls,' said the weedy man whom Simon had hired to carry my bag for the afternoon.

'It's a lost shot as well as a lost ball,' I explained.

'If you can't see it easily you are not going to be able to play it,' said the caddy. 'And if you are worried about the cost of a ball you shouldn't be playing golf.'

My first experience of playing with a caddy wasn't going terribly well. He was a very earnest, very critical fellow and in his company I felt strangely restricted. I didn't say anything to Simon, of course, but with him carrying my bag it seemed that all the fun had gone out of golf.

* * *

'What ball are you playing?' asked Simon's caddy a couple of holes later. The four of us were in the rough, looking for Simon's ball.

'A small white one,' replied Simon who genuinely thought he was being helpful. He held up one hand, with two fingers about an inch apart. 'This sort of size,' he added.

'They have numbers on,' said the caddy drily.

'Yes,' said Simon. He stopped and destroyed a few more weeds by swishing his four iron back and forth. 'But I never hit the same one often enough for it to be worthwhile remembering the number.'

'You shouldn't do that, sir,' said the caddy.

Simon stopped waving his four iron about and looked at him.

'In case you disturb your ball,' explained the caddy.

'Oh yes.'

'Perhaps you should consider playing another,' sighed the caddy, after a look at his watch.

* * *

'That's a huge bunker,' said Simon's caddy. He and my caddy were standing a few feet behind me. Simon was on the green admiring his ball.

'It wasn't a bunker when he started,' I heard my caddy say. 'It was just a divot.'

'Wow,' muttered Simon's caddy. 'I need some foundations digging for my new garage. Do you think we could get him to pop round with his sand iron? I was going to hire a man with a digger but he'd be quicker.' The two caddies sniggered.

I shuffled my feet deeper into the sand and tried to concentrate. Then I swung my club back and hit the ball as hard as I could. It almost buried itself in the face of the bunker. Only a small portion of its surface was visible. If the caddies hadn't been there I'd have dug the ball out with my toe and knocked it out backwards. But I knew I had to plough on, digging myself deeper and deeper into the bunker. It was a nightmare. I felt myself blushing with embarrassment. I hadn't blushed so much since the elastic had gone in my gym shorts and all the girls in my class had seen me in my underpants. I'd been five at the time.

* * *

I can hit a seven iron 130 to 140 yards unless there is a pond or a stream just over 150 yards away in which case I can, if I hold back a little, hit it just over 150 yards.

On the next hole I hit five balls just over 160 yards with my seven iron. All of them landed with a splash instead of a bounce. I used a nine iron for the sixth ball and left it short of the water hazard. I then used a wedge to attempt to hit the ball over the water. Naturally I put the ball into the pond. I swear I could hear both caddies smirking.

* * *

'What club would you recommend here?' I asked.

'It doesn't matter,' replied my caddy wearily. 'Just use an old ball.'

* * *

In frustration, desperation and sheer anger Simon hurled his four iron into the trees. Hands on hips he stood and watched it bounce from branch to branch before clattering down into the undergrowth.

'Do you think we'll find it?' he asked his caddy.

'Dunno, sir,' replied the caddy. 'I think you'd perhaps better throw a provisional.' He offered Simon the bag. 'Which one would you like, sir?' he asked. 'There are quite a few left. I would suggest perhaps an eight iron, sir?'

'Give me the bloody eight iron,' said Simon. 'And don't even look to see what it lands.'

* * *

'I'll take the clubs now,' I said to the caddy, as we left the 18th.

'Are you sure, sir?' he asked, handing me the bag.

'I hope it hasn't been too painful for you,' I said, taking out the £20 note which I had placed in my trouser pocket before the round had started. 'I'm afraid I'm not much of a golfer.'

The caddy thanked me, took the £20 note and carefully placed it in his wallet. He handed me a small brown envelope. 'That's my VAT invoice, sir,' he said.

Surprised, I took the invoice from him and put it into my trouser pocket. I wondered if I dare ask him for my £20 back. I decided I didn't dare.

'I've caddied for a good many men, sir,' he told me with a smirky sort of smile. 'And a few ladies too. But there's not many of them can play the game of golf like yourself. It has been an experience I would not have wanted to have missed.' He handed me a visiting card. It was expensive card and the printing on it was embossed. 'If you need a caddy again would you ring me, sir? It will always be a pleasure to carry your bag.'

I looked down at the card which contained his name, address, telephone number, mobile telephone number, e-mail address, VAT number and company registration number. When I looked up he was gone, walking away towards the car park. I stood for a moment and watched as he unlocked his car, a splendid looking Jaguar XJ6, climbed in and purred away. I opened the envelope he'd given me. It contained two things: an invoice for his services (seventy five pounds plus VAT) and a pre-paid addressed envelope so that I could post him my cheque.

*** *** ***

There is a deep pond to the right of the 18th green. It is rumoured to be bottomless, though I suspect this rumour was deliberately started by the groundsman so that he could have a monopoly on dredging the pond for balls. You have to pass the pond as you walk towards the clubhouse. As we walked past I took my bag off my shoulder and stood for a moment with it in my hands. I then hurled it as far as I could into the pond. The bag and clubs landed with a huge splash and disappeared from sight a moment later.

'I've heard of people doing that,' said Simon, who had appeared out of the evening murk. 'But I've never seen anyone do it before.'

'Why do they make the damned course so difficult to play?' I asked, as we walked off the 18th green.

'I think the idea is to present us with a challenge,' explained Simon

'But my whole life is a challenge!' I protested. 'I don't need a challenge when I'm supposed to be relaxing.' We walked on a few more paces in silence. 'Golf is a bloody stupid game,' I stormed. 'I'm never playing again. What a waste of a day. Whoever it was who said that golf is a good walk spoiled was absolutely spot on.'

'Mark Twain,' said Simon. I looked at him. 'It was Mark Twain who said that.'

We walked on a little further. The clubhouse looked curiously welcoming in the twilight. The lights were all on in the lounge and I could see smoke curling up from the chimney.

'I'm sorry about the caddies,' said Simon. 'Not a great success, were they?'

'Oh, er, well, it was a lovely thought...,' I said tactfully.

'Bloody disaster,' said Simon. 'Seemed a good idea at the time.'

'It was a great idea,' I said.

'Mine gave me a VAT invoice,' said Simon. He looked across at me.

'Mine too,' I laughed.

'Give me yours,' he said.

'Don't be daft.'

'It was a birthday treat.'

'Buy me a whisky when we get into the clubhouse.'

'A large malt will make you feel better,' agreed Simon.

'Laphroaig,' I said. 'I especially enjoy Laphroaig when I'm cold and miserable. It makes me feel warm inside.'

'Laphroaig it is,' agreed Simon.

We walked a little further. It felt strange to be walking towards the golf club without a bag on my shoulder.

* * *

We were sitting in two leather armchairs beside a roaring log fire. I had a glass of Laphroaig in my hand and a few good sips of the life-giving fluid in my stomach.

'Do you fancy a game tomorrow?' asked Simon.

'What time?' I asked.

'About two thirty?'

'That should be OK,' I said.

'It'll just about give us time to finish a round before it gets dark,' said Simon.

'Right,' I said.

We sipped at our whisky.

'Do you know where I can borrow some clubs?'

'I've got a spare set you can borrow,' said Simon.

'Thanks,' I said.

We sipped again.

'I'll pop into the shop on the way home and buy some more balls, tees, gloves, that sort of thing.'

We sipped more whisky.

'I wonder how deep that pond really is.'

'I don't think it's bottomless.'

'Nor do I.'

'Can you remember where you were when you threw them in?'

'I think so.'

'It's dark.'

'That's good. It means no one will see us.'

'Shall we have another whisky first?'

'Oh, I think so.'

Chapter Twenty Two

'The Golf Addict.'

One year after I joined the golf club I worked out that I was spending 40 hours a week working, 56 hours sleeping and 42 hours at the golf club.

My waking life revolved around golf. Most of my friends were golfers. I spent my birthday at the golf club and even visited it on Boxing Day. Most of the presents I had unwrapped for a year had been golf-related. The books and magazines I chose to read were mostly about golf. My annual holiday was a golfing trip taken with Simon. My remaining dreams and ambitions were mostly golf related. I'd had just two more pars since that magical day when I scored my first ever three, but every good shot I played had sharpened my addiction.

I had learned that in some ways the best part of golf is that you can enjoy it when you aren't playing it. Talking about it, dreaming about it, imagining what might happen one day and, finally, giving reality a twist and imagining what did happen. 'Reality is what I remember,' said someone. I think it might have been Anthony Burgess, the novelist. Whoever it was he could well have been talking about golfers.

Simon arrived at the club one day and announced that he had received a generous offer for the freehold of his stationery shop from an estate agency.

'I'm selling up and retiring,' he said. 'I can just about manage it on the money I'm getting for the shop. I shall devote my retirement to golf. I may turn professional next spring.'

* * *

I went along to see my doctor for my annual check-up.

'So, how am I doing?' I asked the doctor when he'd finished prodding and poking.

'Much the same as last time,' he told me. 'You're still alive but you really need to take up some exercise and get more fresh air.'

I reminded him that I'd joined the golf club. He just smiled. 'You seem to be suffering from more stress,' he said. 'Are you under pressure at work?'

'No, no,' I said with certainty.

'So what sort of things do you worry about?'

I thought for a moment. 'My slice,' I said. 'It won't go away. And whether I can afford one of those new American drivers with a head the size of the Isle of Wight.'

'Ah. So the game you took up to improve your health is now causing you stress?

'Oh no, not at all,' I insisted, terrified that he might suddenly ban me from playing. 'I just play for fun. I don't really worry about these things. Not in the sense of 'worry'. I mean I could play much better if I wanted to. I've been told I could play at professional level.'

'Gosh,' said the doctor. 'I'm impressed. Who told you that?'

'Chap I play with called Simon.'

'Ah. Is that the Simon who owns the stationery shop?'

'Oh no. Not him. Not him at all.' I felt myself blushing. I'm a terrible liar. 'No. Well, yes, actually. It may have been him after all. Difficult to remember now. But it doesn't matter anyway because I'm happy just to pootle about and have a bit of fun. Of course if I could break 100 I'd be pretty excited. But I'm not all that bothered to be honest. I always think that if you reach the stars too soon what do you do for an encore? I mean, if I get there too soon I won't have anything left to aim for will I?'

I didn't tell him that my main ambition was still to get round the course with the same ball with which I'd started.

'So you're pretty laid back about the whole thing?'

'Oh yes.' I lied.

'As far as golf is concerned you can take it or leave it?'

'Oh yes. Definitely.'

'I heard you threw your clubs into a pond beside the 18th green because you decided you were going to give up golf. But you had to wade in at night and fish them out so that you could play again the next day.'

'Oh no. That's rubbish.' I insisted. 'Who told you that? I tripped over a tree root and slipped. The clubs just sort of fell in. I left them there while I found out how deep the pond was.'

'The doctor I know who plays golf...

'...the one who wears a bow tie because he's a gynaecologist?'

'That's the one. He says the new bunker they've put on the fifth improves the hole enormously. What do you think about it?'

'Oh that's nonsense!' I said. 'It's in a terrible position. I've always played a driver and a three iron on that hole. The bunker caught my three iron twice last week. I've had to start laying up with a five iron. A few pals and I are going to go out one night and fill it in.'

'How many times a week do you play?'

'Just once or twice.'

'Once or twice?'

'Well perhaps a bit more than that if the weather's good.'

'Every day?'

'Oh no. Not every day.' I said. 'Definitely not every day. I don't always play on Wednesdays.'

He wrote something down on my medical notes. I tried to see what it was but his hand was in the way and I couldn't quite read it.

'Is your mother happy now that you're playing golf regularly?'

'Oh yes, I'm sure she is. She still hopes I might meet a nice young woman there.'

'Marry and settle down?'

'That sort of thing, I suppose.'

'She'd probably be happy for you to give up golf if you got married.'

'Oh no, I don't think so.' I said, shaking my head.

'I'm sure she would.'

'No. No, I don't think so.' I looked at him as if he had gone stark raving mad. 'Why would I want to do that?'

He didn't speak. Just smiled. He moved his hand. I could see it clearly. Even upside down. Just two words.

'Great. Right. I'll see you in a year,' he said.

'Fine. Thanks.'

I left.

'Golf Addict.'

That's what the two words were.

'Golf Addict.'

What rubbish.

I could give up golf whenever I wanted to. If I wanted to. I really could.

For a catalogue of Vernon Coleman's books
please write to:

Publishing House
Trinity Place
Barnstaple
Devon EX32 9HG
England

Telephone   01271 328892
Fax   01271 328768

Outside the UK:
Telephone   +44 1271 328892
Fax   +44 1271 328768

Or visit our website:

www.vernoncoleman.com